MW00861009

## Your Crossword Solving Strategy

Try the following steps for successful solving:

1. **Scan the clues and pick out a clue that you can easily answer.**

   Try looking for missing-word clues first — most people find those the easiest to answer. You don't need to start with 1 Across. Keep scanning the clues until you find one that you can answer.

2. **After you enter an answer for one clue, work on the clues that connect to the clue you already answered.**

3. **Look for three- and four-letter entries in the grid.**

   Shorter entries are sometimes easier to solve. Corners are good places to spot three- and four-letter entries.

4. **Look for theme entries.**

   Some puzzles include longer entries that are connected through a common subject. If you can get the answer to one of these clues and catch on to the trick, then it may help you to solve the other theme-related clues. The theme-related entries are usually the longest entries in the grid.

5. **Keep on cracking until you fill in each square.**

## Puzzle Web Sites to Visit

If you have access to the World Wide Web, check out these great Web sites for puzzles and puzzle tips:

- **Index of Crossword Puzzles:** www.primate.wisc.edu/people/hamel/cp/html
- **The Los Angeles Times:** www.student.net/xwords
- **MacNamara's Band Crossword Puzzles:** www.macnamarasband.com
- **Puzzability:** www.puzzability.com
- **Puzzle Depot:** www.puzzledepot.com/index/shtml
- **The Washington Post:** www.washingtonpost.com/wps-srv/style/crosswords/front.htm
- **Web Word Search:** www.geocities.com/WestHollywood/2555/puzzle.html
- **Word Puzzle of the Week:** www.smartcode.com/isshtml/weekwsk.htm

## Common Clue Characters

- **2 wrds.:** The entry is composed of two words joined together, with no space in between them.
- **?:** When a clue ends in a question mark (?), the corresponding entry is usually a theme clue, a play on words, or both.
- **abbr.:** The entry is abbreviated.
- **e.g.:** Short for *exempli gratia,* meaning for example. The entry is an example of the person or thing alluded to in the clue.
- **et al.:** Short for *et alii,* meaning and others.
- **Fr.:** Stands for French. Means that the entry is in French.
- **Gr.:** Stands for German. Means that the entry is in German.
- **Lt.:** Stands for Latin. Means that the entry is in Latin.

# 101 Crossword Puzzles For Dummies, Volume 5

## Top Ten Abbreviations Beginning with A

1. ABA = "Lawyer's org."
2. AERO = "Space introduction"
3. ANAT = "Med. student's course"
4. ALG = "HS course"
5. APO = "GI's address"
6. ASCAP = "Tunemaker's org."
7. ATM = "24 hr. banker"
8. AWOL = "Army letters"
9. ASST = "Part of TA"
10. APB = "FBI alert"

## Top Ten Musical Terms

1. ARIA = "Operatic solo"
2. IDYL = "Simple pastoral composition"
3. REED = "Musical tongue?"
4. ETUDE = "Chopin composition"
5. FUGUE = "Musical composition"
6. ALLA = "In the style of: mus."
7. VIVO = "Lively: mus."
8. BEL = " — canto (singing style)"
9. LIED = "German song"
10. TEMPO = "Musical speed"

## Roman Numerals

Constructors sometimes use Roman numerals in clues, which usually means that the entry also calls for Roman numerals. For example, you may see a clue such as "Roman 2001," which answers to MMI. Roman numerals have the following numeric equivalents:

- I = 1
- V = 5
- X = 10
- L = 50
- C = 100
- D = 500
- M = 1,000

## Top Ten Abbreviations Beginning with E

1. EPA = "DC watchdog"
2. ERA = "Failed amendment"
3. EST = "Time, in NYC"
4. ETA = "Letters at LAX"
5. ETO = "Ike's WWII post"
6. ET AL = "Common catchall"
7. ECOL = "EPA concern"
8. ETC = "List ender"
9. ESL = "Immigration Dept. requirement"
10. EMU = "New currency org."

## Top Ten Phrases in the Grid

1. AS IS = "Words on a sale tag"
2. IT IS = "How sweet —!"
3. I SEE = "Understanding phrase"
4. TO BE = "Opening of Hamlet's speech"
5. ET TU = "Beginning of Caesar's question"
6. OH NO = "Yikes!"
7. HA HA = "Sounds of laughter"
8. TO NO = "— avail"
9. ON OR = "Words of approximation"
10. I DO = "Wedding vow"

The IDG Books Worldwide logo is a registered trademark under exclusive license to IDG Books Worldwide, Inc., from International Data Group, Inc. The ...For Dummies logo is a trademark, and For Dummies and ...For Dummies are registered trademarks of IDG Books Worldwide, Inc. All other trademarks are the property of their respective owners.

**...For Dummies®: Bestselling Book Series for Beginners**

# Praise for Michelle Arnot and Crossword Puzzles For Dummies

"At long last — a clearly presented, fun answer to all those questions posed to me by 'puzzled' solvers over the years. Michelle Arnot really knows the world of puzzles and has presented a tour of this world that appeals to the novice and the experienced solver."
— Janis Weiner, Editorial Director, Puzzles,
Kappa Publishng Group, Inc.

"Crosswords! Cryptograms! Acrostics! No need to be puzzled any longer. This addition to the IDG library deciphers and reveals the secrets behind the grid. You find out how puzzles are constructed, plus you get insiders' steps and hints, puzzle makers' techniques, along with sample puzzles from the top constructors. Beginners and pros alike will enjoy Michelle Arnot's insight into the world's greatest pastime. She will have you quickly join the millions of puzzlers who delight in word game addiction."
— Marilynn Huret, Editor, At The Crossroads,
www.atthecrossroads.com

"It is a pleasure to endorse Michelle Arnot's sprightly written book, which opens the door to the adventure and joy that is puzzle solving."
— Trude Michel Jaffe, Editor, *Los Angeles Times* Syndicate
Daily Puzzle

"Michelle Arnot is one of the clearest, liveliest, most entertaining writers in the world of puzzles. Here is an excellent beginner's guide to mastering the secrets of crosswords."
— Will Shortz, Crossword Editor, *The New York Times*

# 101 CROSSWORD PUZZLES FOR DUMMIES®

## VOLUME 5

# 101 CROSSWORD PUZZLES FOR DUMMIES® VOLUME 5

## Edited by Michelle Arnot

# IDG BOOKS WORLDWIDE

IDG Books Worldwide, Inc.
An International Data Group Company

Foster City, CA ◆ Chicago, IL ◆ Indianapolis, IN ◆ New York, NY

101 Crossword Puzzles For Dummies® Volume 5

Published by
**IDG Books Worldwide, Inc.**
An International Data Group Company
919 E. Hillsdale Blvd.
Suite 400
Foster City, CA 94404
www.idgbooks.com (IDG Books Worldwide Web site)
www.dummies.com (Dummies Press Web site)

Library of Congress Catalog Card No.: 97-81243

ISBN: 0-7645-5143-4

Printed in the United States of America

10 9 8 7 6 5 4 3 2 1

5B/QZ/QV/ZZ/IN

Distributed in the United States by IDG Books Worldwide, Inc.

Distributed by CDG Books Canada Inc. for Canada; by Transworld Publishers Limited in the United Kingdom; by IDG Norge Books for Norway; by IDG Sweden Books for Sweden; by IDG Books Australia Publishing Corporation Pty. Ltd. for Australia and New Zealand; by TransQuest Publishers Pte Ltd. for Singapore, Malaysia, Thailand, Indonesia, and Hong Kong; by Gotop Information Inc. for Taiwan; by ICG Muse, Inc. for Japan; by Norma Comunicaciones S.A. for Colombia; by Intersoft for South Africa; by Le Monde en Tique for France; by International Thomson Publishing for Germany, Austria and Switzerland; by Distribuidora Cuspide for Argentina; by Livraria Cultura for Brazil; by Ediciones ZETA S.C.R. Ltda. for Peru; by WS Computer Publishing Corporation, Inc., for the Philippines; by Contemporanea de Ediciones for Venezuela; by Express Computer Distributors for the Caribbean and West Indies; by Micronesia Media Distributor, Inc. for Micronesia; by Grupo Editorial Norma S.A. for Guatemala; by Chips Computadoras S.A. de C.V. for Mexico; by Editorial Norma de Panama S.A. for Panama; by American Bookshops for Finland. Authorized Sales Agent: Anthony Rudkin Associates for the Middle East and North Africa.

For general information on IDG Books Worldwide's books in the U.S., please call our Consumer Customer Service department at 800-762-2974. For reseller information, including discounts and premium sales, please call our Reseller Customer Service department at 800-434-3422.

For information on where to purchase IDG Books Worldwide's books outside the U.S., please contact our International Sales department at 317-596-5530 or fax 317-596-5692.

For consumer information on foreign language translations, please contact our Customer Service department at 1-800-434-3422, fax 317-596-5692, or e-mail rights@idgbooks.com.

For information on licensing foreign or domestic rights, please phone +1-650-655-3109.

For sales inquiries and special prices for bulk quantities, please contact our Sales department at 650-655-3200 or write to the address above.

For information on using IDG Books Worldwide's books in the classroom or for ordering examination copies, please contact our Educational Sales department at 800-434-2086 or fax 317-596-5499.

For press review copies, author interviews, or other publicity information, please contact our Public Relations department at 650-655-3000 or fax 650-655-3299.

For authorization to photocopy items for corporate, personal, or educational use, please contact Copyright Clearance Center, 222 Rosewood Drive, Danvers, MA 01923, or fax 978-750-4470.

# About the Editor

A funny thing happened to Michelle Arnot on her way to a Master's degree in 18th century French literature at Columbia University: She ended up making a career of her hobby in crosswords. Instead of writing a thesis, Michelle constructed a crossword. When the puzzle was accepted for publication, she switched gears immediately.

Michelle has been omnipresent in the world of puzzles since the publication of her book *What's Gnu: The History of the Crossword Puzzle* (Vintage Books, 1981). She has served as Editor and Publisher of dozens of national puzzle magazines, most notably for *The Herald Tribune* and the Kappa Publishing Group. Additionally, she taught seminars on solving for the New School For Social Research and the Learning Annex. Her editorial career gradually extended into the marketing of puzzle magazines in the direct mail arena. Michelle edited *101 Crosswords For Dummies,* Volumes 1 through 5, and she is also the author of *Crossword Puzzles For Dummies,* all published by IDG Books Worldwide, Inc.

In her other life, Michelle is a health writer who specializes in subjects of interest to women. She's written books on topics as diverse as infertility and foot care.

When she's not at the word processor, Michelle is often found exploring London, where she currently lives with her husband and daughter. You can easily identify Michelle in warm weather by her T-shirt adorned with a crossword grid.

# ABOUT IDG BOOKS WORLDWIDE

Welcome to the world of IDG Books Worldwide.

IDG Books Worldwide, Inc., is a subsidiary of International Data Group, the world's largest publisher of computer-related information and the leading global provider of information services on information technology. IDG was founded more than 30 years ago by Patrick J. McGovern and now employs more than 9,000 people worldwide. IDG publishes more than 290 computer publications in over 75 countries. More than 90 million people read one or more IDG publications each month.

Launched in 1990, IDG Books Worldwide is today the #1 publisher of best-selling computer books in the United States. We are proud to have received eight awards from the Computer Press Association in recognition of editorial excellence and three from Computer Currents' First Annual Readers' Choice Awards. Our best-selling ...For Dummies® series has more than 50 million copies in print with translations in 31 languages. IDG Books Worldwide, through a joint venture with IDG's Hi-Tech Beijing, became the first U.S. publisher to publish a computer book in the People's Republic of China. In record time, IDG Books Worldwide has become the first choice for millions of readers around the world who want to learn how to better manage their businesses.

Our mission is simple: Every one of our books is designed to bring extra value and skill-building instructions to the reader. Our books are written by experts who understand and care about our readers. The knowledge base of our editorial staff comes from years of experience in publishing, education, and journalism — experience we use to produce books to carry us into the new millennium. In short, we care about books, so we attract the best people. We devote special attention to details such as audience, interior design, use of icons, and illustrations. And because we use an efficient process of authoring, editing, and desktop publishing our books electronically, we can spend more time ensuring superior content and less time on the technicalities of making books.

You can count on our commitment to deliver high-quality books at competitive prices on topics you want to read about. At IDG Books Worldwide, we continue in the IDG tradition of delivering quality for more than 30 years. You'll find no better book on a subject than one from IDG Books Worldwide.

John Kilcullen
Chairman and CEO
IDG Books Worldwide, Inc.

Steven Berkowitz
President and Publisher
IDG Books Worldwide, Inc.

Eighth Annual
Computer Press
Awards ≥ 1992

Ninth Annual
Computer Press
Awards ≥ 1993

Tenth Annual
Computer Press
Awards ≥ 1994

Eleventh Annual
Computer Press
Awards ≥ 1995

# Dedication

To my husband Roger and daughter Astrid, who make time outside puzzles worthwhile!

# Editor's Acknowledgments

Once again, a stellar group of talented constructors provided the puzzles that fill this fine collection. Thanks go (in alphabetical order) to: James Beatty, Janet R. Bender, Mary E. Brindamour, Gayle Dean, Bernice Gordon, Geraldine S. Harris, Randall J. Hartman, Julia Hess, Alfio Micci, Gregory E. Paul, Fred Piscop, Nancy Salomon, and Jay Sullivan. Extra special thanks to Marilynn Huret of www.atthecrossroads.com for her valuable contribution, and to my technical editor Diana Conover.

Just like for Volumes 1, 2, 3, and 4 of *101 Crossword Puzzles For Dummies*, sincere thanks to my longterm editor, Mary Goodwin, for getting me through 505 puzzles in record time. Her insight, direction, genuine interest, and endless patience maintained a productive working relationship that has extended over six books and one ocean. All best wishes on her upcoming wedding, which she's been planning in her spare time! Here's to Mary and the most fortunate "Mr. Right"!

Traveling through the land of puzzles, I've been fortunate to meet scores of folks in all aspects of the field who have influenced me and generously shared their knowledge. Among these talented professionals, special thanks to puzzle titans Nancy Schuster, Will Shortz, and Stan Newman. Lastly, thank you to the Kappa Publishing Group, with which I've had the pleasure of being affiliated for more than a dozen years.

# Publisher's Acknowledgments

We're proud of this book; please register your comments through our IDG Books Worldwide Online Registration Form located at http://my2cents.dummies.com.

Some of the people who helped bring this book to market include the following:

### Acquisitions and Editorial

**Project Editor:** Mary Goodwin

**Senior Acquisitions Editor:** Mark Butler

**Acquisitions Coordinator:** Jonathan Malysiak

**Editorial Coordinator:** Maureen F. Kelly

**Copy Editors:** Stephanie Koutek, Donna Love

**Technical Editor:** Diana Conover

**Editorial Manager:** Kelly Ewing

**Editorial Assistant:** Paul E. Kuzmic

### Production

**Project Coordinator:** Tom Missler

**Layout and Graphics:** Linda M. Boyer, Angela F. Hunckler, Anna Rohrer, Brent Savage, Janet Seib, Jacque Schneider, Brian Torwelle

**Proofreaders:** Arielle Carole Mennelle, Nancy Price, Ethel Winslow, Janet M. Withers

### General and Administrative

**IDG Books Worldwide, Inc.:** John Kilcullen, CEO; Steven Berkowitz, President and Publisher

**IDG Books Technology Publishing Group:** Richard Swadley, Senior Vice President and Publisher; Walter Bruce III, Vice President and Associate Publisher; Steven Sayre, Associate Publisher; Joseph Wikert, Associate Publisher; Mary Bednarek, Branded Product Development Director; Mary Corder, Editorial Director

**IDG Books Consumer Publishing Group:** Roland Elgey, Senior Vice President and Publisher; Kathleen A. Welton, Vice President and Publisher; Kevin Thornton, Acquisitions Manager; Kristin A. Cocks, Editorial Director

**IDG Books Internet Publishing Group:** Brenda McLaughlin, Senior Vice President and Publisher; Diane Steele, Vice President and Associate Publisher; Sofia Marchant, Online Marketing Manager

**IDG Books Production for Dummies Press:** Michael R. Britton, Vice President of Production; Debbie Stailey, Associate Director of Production; Cindy L. Phipps, Manager of Project Coordination, Production Proofreading, and Indexing; Laura Carpenter, Production Control Manager; Shelley Lea, Supervisor of Graphics and Design; Debbie J. Gates, Production Systems Specialist; Robert Springer, Supervisor of Proofreading; Tony Augsburger, Supervisor of Reprints and Bluelines

**Dummies Packaging and Book Design:** Patty Page, Manager, Promotions Marketing

♦

The publisher would like to give special thanks to Patrick J. McGovern, without whom this book would not have been possible.

♦

# Contents at a Glance

# Cartoons at a Glance

*By Rich Tennant*

"This is a weekly publication. Make me a crossword puzzle with a solution time of 168 hours."

**page 5**

"It's Deep Blue. After beating Garry Kasparov in chess, we tried feeding it The New York Times crossword puzzle, and after about an hour, the whole thing just crashed."

**page 71**

**page 113**

"Oscar Mellen's a great puzzler, but he's never been able to attend this convention primarily because there's no common letter in his first and last name."

**page 129**

"Looks like a slow news day."

**page 143**

*Fax:* 978-546-7747 • *E-mail:* the5wave@tiac.net

# Table of Contents

## Part II: Sunday Puzzle Fun ................................................................. 71

## Part III: Other Puzzle Fun ................................................................. 113

# Introduction

A head of chess, bingo, checkers, and bridge, crossword puzzle solving is America's most popular brain food. In fact, baby boomers rank puzzles at the top of their daily routines, right alongside eating. It's no coincidence that 99.9 percent of newspapers in the U. S. carry a crossword in their pages — many people can't start the day without their daily puzzle.

In *101 Crossword Puzzles For Dummies,* Volume 5, you find a style of puzzle to suit every taste. (If you haven't figured out your style yet, the puzzles on the following pages may help you make up your mind.) Feel free to indulge yourself. This is one habit you don't have to feel guilty about: It's calorie-free and guaranteed to lower your blood pressure.

If something about those little square diagrams reminds you of the SAT, put that thought behind you once and for all. Don't think of puzzles as a test; no one is looking over your shoulder. And you don't have a time limit besides the one you set for yourself. Puzzles should relax, distract, and amuse. True, you may discover some new tidbit of information or recall some facts from the deepest reaches of your brain, but these are just side effects to the real focus of puzzles, which is fun.

If you are totally new to the world of puzzles, you should consider picking up a copy of my other book, *Crossword Puzzles For Dummies,* published by IDG Books Worldwide, Inc. *Crossword Puzzles For Dummies* is chock-full of solving tips and strategies to get you started.

## Why a ...For Dummies Crossword Puzzle Book?

Yes, this book is different from those other puzzle books you see on the shelf or in the bins in the supermarket (you know, right next to the *National Enquirer*). *101 Crosswords Puzzles For Dummies,* Volume 5, delivers puzzles, puzzles, puzzles in a way that makes them easy and more fun to work:

- You get 101 puzzles that people actually like to work, including daily-size crosswords, Sunday-size crosswords, acrostics, diagramlesses, and cryptograms.

- The puzzles make use of today's most common *repeaters,* or words that frequently appear in crossword puzzles.

- The puzzles vary in theme and difficulty, but none of the puzzles is insurmountable. I provide solving tips and hints when I think you may appreciate a boost.

- The clues are easy to read, and the grid blocks allow you plenty of room to pencil in your answer.

- You have room in the margins and around the page to doodle with possible entries before you enter them in the grid.

- You always find the grid located close to the outside of the page, making it easy to write in your answers.

✔ Each puzzle has a number (and sometimes a name), making it easy for you to find the answers to your puzzle in Appendix A.

✔ I make the answer grids large enough so that you can actually read them. Go ahead and put away that magnifying glass.

# How to Use This Book

I divide this book into five parts:

## Part I: A Dose of Daily Puzzles

Every puzzle in this part is 15 x 15 squares, which should be the perfect size puzzle to conquer during your lunch break.

## Part II: Sunday Puzzle Fun

The puzzles in this part are generally 21 x 21 squares, which means that you may need to set aside some time to enjoy these puzzles. Most of the puzzles offer a theme to add to your solving pleasure.

## Part III: Other Puzzle Fun

What does it take to be a "non-crossword" puzzle? In Part III, you find cryptograms, acrostics, and diagramless puzzles waiting for your amusement. Visit this part of the book for a little variety in your puzzle life.

## Part IV: The Part of Tens

Part IV offers a quick guide to some names that appear frequently in puzzles. I also list several entries that appear time and time again in puzzles.

## Part V: Appendixes

You get to satisfy your curiosity in this part. Appendix A contains the answers to all the puzzles in the book. Appendix B offers a guiding hand to working the non-crossword puzzles you find in Part III.

# Icons Used in This Book

I use icons periodically throughout this book to point out important tips and topics that I want you to know.

As in any game, puzzles have rules, both written and unwritten. Just to make sure that you're on your toes, this icon reminds you of these important rules.

Next to this icon you find advice and information that can make you a savvier solver.

Sometimes I offer hints on how to solve particular puzzles in the book. If you'd rather take a crack at the puzzle without my help, this icon steers you clear of any information that may spoil the challenge for you.

4 **101 Crossword Puzzles For Dummies, Volume 5**

# Part I
# A Dose of Daily Puzzles

The 5th Wave    By Rich Tennant

"This is a weekly publication. Make me a crossword puzzle with a solution time of 168 hours."

# Puzzle 1-1: Names in Mystery

Another clue for 28 Down is "Word meaning 'I give up!'"

## Across

1 Double agent
5 Spaghetti sauce
10 Randy Barne throws it
14 *Jeopardy* host Trebek
15 Singer Hoyt
16 Rushed headlong
17 Jai —
18 Name in mystery
20 Informed, mob-style
21 Folsom gathering place
22 Mr. T's series, after *The*
23 Warren of the Supreme Court
25 "Thrilla in Manila" winner
26 Name in mystery
32 Dry up
33 "Far out!"
34 Sticky place
36 *The Picture of Dorian —*
37 Kevin of *Footloose*
39 Wild pig
40 Follow in Liz Taylor's steps
41 Spinnaker
42 Fonda senior
43 Name in mystery
47 Costs an — and a leg
48 City on the Oka
49 Iowa society

52 Like an eagle
54 Don Juan's mom
58 Name in mystery
60 Knot
61 Gallimaufry
62 Older companion
63 Dec. 24 and 31
64 Coal stratum
65 Lacks
66 Carry on

## Down

1 *Serpico* author Peter
2 Earthen jar
3 Jack Sprat's diet, e.g.
4 Critical situation
5 Egyptian reading materials
6 *Waiting to —* (Terry McMillan)
7 Mix it up
8 Related
9 Plastic-Band link
10 Word with cling
11 Sharpen
12 Quint's boat in *Jaws*
13 Swarm
19 Man Friday
24 Fire proof
25 Hawkeye portrayer Alda
26 *Little Women* family
27 Emulate Demosthenes
28 Napoleon Solo's employer
29 — Speedwagon
30 Maine college town
31 Milk measure
32 Tiger Woods' org.
35 "Give it a —!"
37 *The Wizard of Oz* author
38 Feel poorly
39 "Ich bin ein —" (JFK)
41 "Out!"
42 Hurry up, old-style
44 *The — of Red Chief*
45 Took a survey
46 Uses a menu
49 Andy's partner
50 Race for Roger Bannister
51 Populous continent
52 Soft cheese
53 Church recess
55 Hubble Telescope sight
56 Land west of Nod
57 Piquancy
59 Barley bristle

# Puzzle 1-2: Strange Sightings

Some entries are two short words. (See 4 and 49 Down.)

## Across

1 Rainbows
5 Thanksgiving side dish
9 Play a uke
14 Gwen Verdon role
15 Square footage
16 "— porridge hot . . ."
17 Oil of —
18 Get cozy
19 Like a beaver
20 Strange sighting
23 Irritable
24 Diviner's implement
25 Apply powder
28 Gains mastery of
32 Chophouse request
33 Never
36 Early Greek colony
37 Strange sighting
40 *Angela's* — (Frank McCourt book)
41 North Carolina native
42 "— there, done that"
43 Mob, after *Cosa*
45 Old-time neighbor of Scand.
46 Tit-tat link
47 Scottish landowner
52 Strange sighting
56 Computer timesaver
59 Mayberry kid
60 Amass, with "up"
61 "Old Macdonald" refrain
62 Sailor's cry
63 At any time
64 In a quandary
65 *Cogito* — *sum*
66 Final figures, after tax

## Down

1 Up in the air
2 TV actress Esther
3 Statesman Henry and family
4 "— ain't so, Joe!"
5 Yin's counterpart
6 Bellicose deity
7 Flat-topped elevation
8 Ringed planet
9 Exceed the limit
10 Get dewy-eyed
11 Tease
12 Take advantage of
13 Debussy's *La* —

21 Stockings
22 Funnyman Bill, familiarly
25 Beatrice's admirer
26 Sharon of Israel
27 Wall Street pessimist
29 Suffix with ethyl
30 Fund-raising health org.
31 Takes a breather
32 The all-time hit leader
33 Snoops
34 Autumn color
35 In that case
36 Aerobics instructor's command
37 Chem. rooms
38 Welcome —
39 Hockey legend Bobby
43 Armistice mo.
44 Bird on a baseball cap
46 Basement problem
48 Quaking tree
49 "As — and breathe!"
50 Rent again
51 Salon specialists
52 Cleveland's lake
53 Practice pugilism
54 Ricochet sound
55 Take from the top
56 Ran across
57 Tune
58 Middling mark

# Puzzle 1-3: At the Sweet Shoppe

## Across

1 Canary's remark
6 Door position
10 Gather
14 TV hostess O'Donnell
15 A handful
16 Ultimatum word
17 About the bees
18 Sweet shoppe treat
20 Manuscripts, for short
21 "Once — a time . . ."
23 William Jennings Bryan, e.g.
24 Jazz style
25 Buttresses
26 Easy put-on
29 Tureen go-with
30 Chew the scenery
31 River outside Paris
32 Tread
36 Sank one's teeth into
37 Undermine
40 Skater Midori
41 Effort
43 Playwright Coward
44 Type of numeral
46 Enjoys
48 Unconditionally
49 North Star
52 Teeming

53 Female warrior
54 Filet mignon, e.g.
55 Hell, according to Sherman
58 Sweet shoppe treat
60 Author Garcia —
62 Alaska's first governor
63 C&W singer Lovett
64 Occasion
65 Talk back
66 Raise one's voice
67 Trig terms

## Down

1 Study feverishly
2 Beer ingredient
3 Sister of Osiris
4 Inlet
5 Sweet shoppe treats
6 British race track
7 One of the Fab Four
8 Beginning Latin verb
9 Simple woodwind
10 Tightens an ice skate
11 Evoke happiness
12 Socialite Brooke
13 House of Lords members
19 Voiced
22 Bit of butter
24 Mil. rank
25 Swiss city on the Rhine
26 Spidery sites
27 Utter
28 Greek letter
29 Dwells
31 Woodwinds
33 Weekly magazine
34 Common catchall
35 — Express
38 With malice
39 Sweet shoppe treats
42 Coats of arms
45 Miner's find
47 Press
48 As American as apple —
49 Loses color
50 Alpha's counterpart
51 Tibetan monks
52 Drive off
54 Cotton seed-capsule
55 St. Paul's architect Christopher
56 Dermatological subject
57 Mild expletive
59 Type of bread or whiskey
61 Leader for duct or form

# *Puzzle 1-4: P.M. Magazine*

Roman numerals are nifty ways of stringing together consonants in puzzles, as in 41 Down.

## Across

1 Speed skater Heiden
5 Two per schooner, usually
10 Pitch a tent
14 *Peter Pan* pooch
15 — nous (confidentially)
16 Diamond stats
17 Italian wine region
18 Cleaner's challenge
19 Give the boot (to)
20 Horse show
23 Quartet quarter
24 Verve
25 Treat without respect
27 Heading
28 Consume
31 Designer Norma
33 Aimless
36 Dill
37 Ezekiel and Jeremiah, e.g.
41 *Laura* actor Andrews
42 Salvation Army seasonal recruits
43 Florida export
46 Choke
47 African runner
50 — de la Cite, Paris
51 Cheerleader's cheers
54 Hank of baseball
56 *L.A. Law* name
60 Make fast
61 Shine
62 Autobahn sight
63 Use a keyboard
64 Kate Nelligan film
65 English word for 50 Across
66 Cruising
67 More burned up
68 Twenty has two

## Down

1 Makes into law
2 Allergy symptoms
3 Harmonious
4 Egypt's capital
5 Net
6 Contrarian, often
7 Like old bread or news
8 Harpsichordist's flourish
9 Author Maurice
10 Boast
11 More than enough
12 Sometimes stored in silos
13 Time in CA
21 System of belief
22 "— clear day . . ."
26 Pose
29 Letters at the depot
30 Bill add-ons
32 West and others
33 Still open
34 Lippo Lippi, e.g.
35 Chinese secret society
37 Junior employees
38 African runner
39 School org.
40 Horrible name in comics
41 Monumental 601
44 First name in spoon bending
45 Base bigwigs
47 Crab
48 Thinking cap
49 Victoria's Secret purchase
52 "Howdy"
53 Lip curl
55 Anticipate
57 Zone
58 Hamlet is one
59 Islamic ruler
60 Bus drivers' org.

# Puzzle 1-5: Sob Stories

Black Beauty is crossword code for "horse" as in 55 Across.

## Across

1 Rocky tor
5 Baby buggy
9 Stinging insects
14 What she wanted, she got
15 Pumice source
16 Dwight beat him
17 *Jake's Thing* author
18 After a bit
19 Motown team
20 Sad trees?
23 Michael, to Kirk
24 Once named
25 Adversaries
26 Drama part
27 "Let no man — asunder"
28 Haw's partner
31 Puccini's genre
34 Gold or star trailer
35 Put to sleep
36 Sadly all wet?
39 Engage
40 Folk singer Burl
41 Polished
42 Visit
43 Stole second
44 Down or up leader
45 Cerise and carmine
46 Wine cask

47 Dress finely, with up or out
50 Sad structure?
54 Coronet
55 Black Beauty's dinner
56 Pickup shaft
57 Place of worship
58 Shade of green
59 Gold source
60 Combine
61 Editorial term
62 West of Nod

## Down

1 Talons
2 Juliet's beloved
3 Sigourney Weaver thriller of '79
4 Shocked sound
5 Mars, e.g.
6 Where the deer and the antelope play
7 Declare
8 Lading lists
9 *The Bridges of Madison County* author
10 Senorita's sign-off
11 Like a snail
12 Gives thumbs-down
13 Before "boom bah"
21 Machu Picchu man
22 Reluctant
26 Racer Luyendyk
27 Adjusted the Steinway
28 Hoodwink
29 Border lake
30 Darn
31 Publisher Adolph
32 Kneeler, with "-dieu"
33 *Jane* —
34 Major military units
35 Angelica of *Rugrats*
37 Funny lady Radner
38 *Dallas* dynasty
43 Purchaser of Alaska
44 Beginning of twilight
45 Aired again
46 Lord or Dame
47 Levied
48 Stan's buddy
49 Astronaut John
50 Cashier's drawer
51 Dislike
52 Café au —
53 High sign
54 Hunter of screen

# Puzzle 1-6: Hidden Grade

## Across

1 Rare bear
6 First of men
10 Ruffian
14 Then, in Tours
15 Editorial note
16 Grimm villain
17 Steel support
18 Pot of Spain
19 Swedish politician Palme
20 Without feeling
23 Poets' "before"
24 Brouhaha
25 Sinatra theme song "My —"
28 Before esses
30 Came back (with)
35 Regretful phrase
37 Shells
39 Numbers game?
40 Complete
43 Terra —
44 Ship's spine
45 Skid
46 Bantu language
48 JFK sight
50 Beth, to Jo or Amy
51 Aperture
53 Man-mouse link
55 Extinct bird
63 White House office
64 Mrs. Chaplin
65 Beau
66 "— but not forgotten"
67 He has recriminations
68 "'Tis better to have — and lost . . ."
69 Charged
70 Kitchen closer
71 Eared vessels

## Down

1 Cashier's stamp
2 Toulouse-Lautrec's birthplace
3 Refusals
4 Hang in folds
5 Capital of Eritrea
6 Commotions
7 Pastrami palaces
8 Elements with multiple molecular forms
9 Nasty one
10 Jeer
11 Give the once-over
12 Exam type
13 Challenge
21 Glacial pinnacle
22 Graceful steeds
25 WWII group
26 Permit
27 WWII big three city
29 Stupefying (as bees)
31 Irish luck
32 Follows
33 Serious boredom
34 Venetian palace owners
36 Eve's third
38 — Tussaud's Wax Mus.
41 Gullible
42 Columnist Joseph
47 Poe maiden
49 Paltry matter
52 Belief
54 Shining
55 Kelly's possum
56 Declare
57 All there
58 Winter vehicle
59 Unusual
60 Overhang
61 Hebrew measure
62 Rorem and namesakes

# Puzzle 1-7: Play Ball!

The term "brief" in a clue is crosswordese for "abbreviated." (See 1 Across.)

## Across

1 Brief returns?
5 Laundromat unit
9 Attorney—
14 Scads
15 —- European
16 *Rocky* actress Talia
17 Latvian capital
18 Navy diver
19 Trapped, like a cat
20 Enjoyed a flick a la Mike Piazza?
23 Slow-witted
24 — Lanka
25 Inland Russian sea
29 Scientific abbr.
31 Subject for Thoreau
33 Unanimously, after "to"
36 Given to wordplay
39 Hogwash
40 Flirted a la Mark McGwire?
44 H'way
45 Sandwich shops
46 Nautical term
47 Ark's landing spot
49 Swing
52 Performer with no lines
53 Onager
56 Boxer's battlefield
59 Went camping a la Randy Johnson?
63 World-weary
66 Marathon, e.g.
67 British "Ciao!"
68 Sheepish
69 Approximately, with "about"
70 School for princes
71 Borscht basis
72 Scout groups
73 Top 40 nominee

## Down

1 Jeanne — (French saint)
2 Tale of Troy
3 Fashion magazine
4 In a rut
5 Prick up one's ears
6 Eligible, military-wise
7 John or John Q.
8 Sorrow
9 Italian wine center
10 Impending danger
11 Tell it like it isn't
12 *Men — from Mars . . .*
13 Tie the knot
21 Before DDE
22 *My Cousin —* (Joe Pesci film)
26 The sticks, e.g.
27 Cropped up
28 River of forgetfulness
30 Common birthstone
32 Assent
33 James — Garfield
34 Prefix meaning "mother"
35 First-stringers
37 Prefix with corn or cycle
38 Loch of legend
41 Author LeShan
42 Coup — (revolution)
43 Newborns' outfits
48 Say an Act of Contrition
50 Fisherman's gear
51 Neighbor of Scorpius
54 Boston catch
55 Classic Alan Ladd Western
57 "Peachy!"
58 Playwright Chekhov
60 Bad day for Caesar
61 M.B.A. subject
62 Chinese dynasty
63 Exemplar of patience
64 St. crosser
65 Parcheesi cube

# Puzzle 1-8: Starring John Travolta

An alternate clue for 52 Down is "Tennessee — Ford."

## Across

**1** Zest
**6** Mess hall meal
**10** Barely managed, with "out"
**14** Pale
**15** Faith-charity connection
**16** Ready for plucking
**17** Travolta film
**20** Barbie's date
**21** Everything but the kitchen —
**22** Actress Blakley
**23** Do again
**25** Health plan acronym
**27** Picnic shade provider
**28** Mrs. Roosevelt
**29** IBM compatibles
**32** Travolta film
**36** Butter measure
**37** Son of Aphrodite
**38** Kurosawa epic
**39** Court figure Sampras
**40** Disencumber
**41** Travolta film
**45** Employ
**46** Facility
**47** *Kojiki* author
**48** Epsom and smelling
**50** Fancy
**53** Dom DeLuise comedy
**55** Make the wild mild
**56** Exist
**58** Travolta film
**62** Charles's sister
**63** Wings, Latin style
**64** Croesus conquest
**65** "All You — Is Love"
**66** Beach bird
**67** Saw regularly

## Down

**1** Stare at
**2** Theater guide
**3** "Rise and —"
**4** Asian holiday
**5** Keep to — (solitary)
**6** Mantra
**7** Gooselike warning
**8** Spouse of Saturn
**9** Part of WWW
**10** Faux pas
**11** R.L. Stevenson character
**12** Fleuret's kin
**13** Valley
**18** Ohio river
**19** — *Cowboy* (Travolta film)
**24** Energizes, with "up"
**25** *Alfie* portrayer Michael
**26** Stella d'— (cookie brand)
**28** Fence pole
**30** Marcus Porcius
**31** Slumgullion, e.g.
**32** Indiana's circus city
**33** *Battle Cry* author Leon
**34** Piece of magnetite
**35** "— patch, lift the latch . . . "
**39** Malayan sailboat
**41** Sailor's retreat
**42** Hamelin pest
**43** Bellini work
**44** Earthworm, e.g.
**49** Posed a poser
**50** Containing Avena grass seeds
**51** Contaminate
**52** Bert's pal on *Sesame Street*
**53** Custard treat
**54** Top-drawer
**55** Winter Palace resident
**57** "Yipes"
**59** Bowler, e.g.
**60** Corrida cheer
**61** Hawaiian timber tree

# Puzzle 1-9: Horizontal 15s

Another way to look at 27 Across is "Brainstorm in Paris."

## Across

1 Finger
8 Spielberg film
15 Albert Finney film of 1984
17 Western Mediterranean group
18 Bend in timber
19 "In — veritas"
20 Former religious practice
21 Purge a guilty conscience
23 Facing the ice
24 Gift giver
27 — fixe
29 Ethiopian capital
33 Indian prince
37 Narc's employer
38 Biblical scholar
40 Sailor
41 Gets down on one knee
43 Like some sports
45 African fox
47 Silly
48 Mink's cousin
51 Skill
55 Golfer Mark
57 Straightedge
58 NCO
61 *Men in Black* actress

64 Pulitzer-winning novel of '96
65 Last course
66 They crave 65 Across

## Down

1 Bars, in Bath
2 — even keel
3 In an aimless way
4 Maiden name lead-in
5 Cross
6 Like a partially raised anchor
7 "Drink to me only with — . . ."
8 Prefix for culture or fauna
9 Rock cover
10 Treat badly
11 Disperse
12 Musical direction
13 Aconcagua's range
14 Medicinal amounts
16 Greenspan's domain, for short
21 Louis XVI, par exemple
22 Roman river
24 Baby's second word
25 Lyric output
26 Neighbor of Minn.
28 Info
30 Jimi Hendrix album — *Bold As Love*
31 Poet Stephen Vincent
32 10 pcter.
34 Taj Mahal site
35 Actress Allen
36 Cap follower
39 Title for the Cardinal
42 Nicoise, and others
44 Track down, Cockney style
46 Shawl in San Juan
48 Like a rock
49 Chemical compound
50 Curves
52 1996 AL batting champ, for short
53 Enticed
54 Kate Nelligan movie
56 Southwest wind
58 Ally oneself with
59 Unfriendly sound
60 Santa's goodies
62 Passbook abbr.
63 Vietnamese holiday

# Puzzle 1-10: Map Reading

Old time TV shows rerun forever in puzzles, especially popular ones like *The Honeymooners*. A straightforward alternate clue for 64 Across is "Subterranean conduit."

## Across

1 Takes a 747
5 High above
10 Carl Lewis's specialty
14 Glassmaker's ingredient
15 Senator William Edgar —
16 Great land mass
17 Nut-bearing tree
18 Like Elvis's blue shoes
19 Caged, with "up"
20 Olsen-Johnson 1939 play at the Broadhurst
23 Flippers
24 Hightailed it
25 Cover with oil
28 Seine stopovers
30 Type of nut
33 Mustang and others
34 Windblown loamy soil deposit
35 Cpl.'s mailbox
36 Michael Landon TV series
40 Zsa Zsa's sister
41 Scottish island
42 "With this — I thee wed"
43 Scout unit
44 "— corny as Kansas . . ."
45 Destroys, as documents
47 Cigarette tip
48 Samoan capital
49 Song from *Maytime*
56 Sun Devils' home, for short
57 Casanova
58 Attire
60 Concerning
61 Ham it up
62 Like Goya's Maja
63 Ottoman officials
64 Norton's workplace
65 Dross

## Down

1 Queens dest.
2 Piccadilly figure
3 Pinball problem
4 Seaside souvenir
5 Part of AWOL
6 Oafs
7 Hematite and galena
8 Sad Portuguese song style
9 — *Prince of Bel-Air*
10 Decorative varnish coating
11 Computer buff
12 Skirt or van opener
13 Strokes
21 One, in Essen
22 Out-of-date
25 Hankered for
26 Green
27 J.S. Bach's instrument
28 Greek letters
29 Spinks of the ring
30 Piaf song "— en Rose"
31 Defeat
32 Big Ben beats
34 Vega's constellation
37 Belt's hangout
38 Vest openings
39 Books
45 On the meager side
46 Secreted
47 Cutting tools
48 Crested ridge
49 Foray
50 Novelist Sarah — Jewett
51 Ethereal
52 Apple, e.g.
53 Declare
54 First king of Israel
55 Wagnerian goddess
59 Implore

# Puzzle 1-11: Hard Stuff

## Across

1 Prepare the laundry
5 Chou —
10 Soul's partner
14 Naval enlisted rank
15 Boxing unit
16 One of HOMES
17 Pawn
18 Popular hymn
20 Annoy
21 100 yrs.
22 Andes ruminant
23 Worked into a lather
25 Bog product
26 Lottery picks, for short
29 Edible fungus
30 Actor Dillon
31 CD
32 Actor Delon
34 Black Sea port
36 Symbol of strength
40 Run in
41 Jai alai basket
42 Screen click-on
43 Actress Sommer
45 Sign up
49 Okays, in Odessa
50 Town in upstate New York
51 Tongue and —

52 Finnish bath
54 *Swan Lake* step
55 — culpa
56 Like some sale prices
59 Mend
60 Needle case
61 Busiest airport
62 Reverse
63 Letters on an envelope
64 Head-shoulder connectors
65 Windfall

## Down

1 Rift
2 City on the Douro
3 Off one's — (batty)
4 Sound of disapproval
5 Made a mistake
6 High time
7 Jean-— Godard
8 Short sock
9 Worshippers of Baal
10 Big grin
11 Church musician
12 Tool and — maker
13 Word of acceptance
19 "Living off the — of the land"
21 Yo-yo Ma's strings
24 Fade out
25 Nervous
27 Greek peak
28 Capone feature
30 Russian fighter plane
31 Franklin — Roosevelt
33 P.M.
35 Librarian's stamps
36 Foray
37 Killer whale
38 Type of saw
39 Busy as a —
44 Detest
46 Parmesan alternative
47 Exhaust oneself
48 "We all need someone to — . . ."
50 Rub-a-dub-dub vessel
51 Popular puzzle magazine
53 Related to
54 Type of governmental barrel?
56 *Michael Collins* actor Stephen
57 Baseball's Mel
58 Tic-toe center
59 Add sound

# Puzzle 1-12: Family Affair

## Across

1 Comedian George
7 Dutch farmer
11 Qty.
14 *Laurence of Arabia* portrayer
15 Albany's canal
16 Actress Wallace-Stone
17 Top 40 entry
19 007 creator Fleming
20 "Rue Morgue" culprit
21 *Happy Days* extra
22 *The X-Files* extra
24 Decision-making time
28 Directly
30 — glance
31 Wanted to know
32 Shelf fillers
38 Sault — Marie
39 Steed
40 Mrs. Peron
41 Seeming contradictions
44 Mythical underworld
46 Powerful D.C. lobby
47 Rolled tobacco leaves
48 Michelangelo masterpiece
54 Zinger from Letterman
55 *The Ghost and Mrs.* —
56 Polluter's bane: abbr.
59 Rural expanse
60 James Stewart Western of 1950
64 Tank
65 It's better than never
66 Prep school town
67 — Miss
68 She sheep
69 Immature

## Down

1 N.Y.C. nightclub, after "The"
2 Over
3 Hemp hauler, perhaps
4 Hall-of-Famer Gehrig
5 Out of commission
6 Put in order
7 Plague
8 Maine college town
9 German article
10 Ketch match
11 Farewell
12 Intended
13 Kegler's last frame
18 Stimpy's pal

23 Snatch
25 Shelley creation
26 TV oldie *The — Squad*
27 Accessory after the —
28 Straplike metal fastener
29 "Como — usted?"
32 Swing in a ring
33 Wish one hadn't
34 Elected types
35 Warnings on the *Enterprise*
36 State
37 Mama of note
39 Lament
42 Opponent
43 Emulate Reggie Miller
44 Cool
45 Historic period
47 Ed Norton portrayer
48 A sudden burst, as of fireworks
49 Perfect
50 List of candidates
51 Chew the scenery
52 Cool veggies
53 Hurry, old-style
57 Frost, e.g.
58 Haywire
61 Like some recruits
62 Cut
63 New Deal power agency

# Puzzle 1-13: Steinbeck Sampler

This puzzle is a quick review of the classic work of 20th century American novelist John Steinbeck.

## Across

1 Units of work
5 It's no lie
9 Joined seamlessly
14 Folktales
15 Cold capital
16 Enlist
17 Maxi feature
18 Peruse Proust
19 — and desist order
20 Steinbeck work
23 Aegean isle
24 Proverb
28 One Blues Brother
32 Retirement letters
33 *I Spy* costar
37 Steinbeck work
39 *Paper Moon* player
41 — volente
42 It's in
43 Steinbeck work
46 Charlie Brown remark
47 Mealtime scrap
48 Foe of 71 Across
50 Protozoan
52 Proverbs
57 Steinbeck work
61 Crew member

64 Laugh riot
65 Seine feeder
66 Battery terminal
67 Four Corners state
68 Concert halls
69 Character builders
70 Suffix with mono or poly
71 See 48 Across

## Down

1 Newspaper south of the border
2 Pocahontas's husband
3 Noted story maker
4 Become ensconced
5 Predict
6 On the briny
7 The Mackenzies, e.g.
8 *Sweeney* —
9 New look
10 Overturn
11 Resort
12 Ernie of golf
13 Change color
21 Pen pal?
22 Hawaiian bird
25 Cassette option
26 "— we a pair . . ." ("Send in the Clowns")
27 Magicians' props
29 *The — Not for Burning*
30 Mouse movers
31 Type of pigeon
33 Winter warmer
34 Take the rod
35 Slowly: mus.
36 Dead end?
38 Slip up
40 Skier's vulnerabilities
44 Keister
45 In the money
49 Letters on a can
51 Chopin composition
53 Under way
54 Skim the surface
55 Stand for a portrait
56 Bargain
58 Gorilla
59 Tittle
60 Potting soil
61 Work at the checkout
62 Singleton
63 Elam, to Shem

# Puzzle 1-14: Rhyme Scheme

Certain crossword compatible names guarantee a slot in the Crossword Hall of Fame, as per 72 Across.

## Across

**1** Chocolate substitute
**6** Rainbows
**10** Nobelist Wiesel
**14** Manila hemp
**15** Tigger's pal
**16** Warrior princess of TV
**17** Wagon train cry
**19** *Meet Joe Black* star
**20** Girds one's loins
**21** Mama razorback
**22** Where to find Vientiane
**23** D'Urbervilles girl
**25** Konishiki's sport
**27** D.C. type
**30** Monopoly card admonition
**35** *Planet of the —*
**37** Actor Silver
**38** Barry Levinson film of '82
**39** Tiber tributary
**40** Beatles' hit "— and Shout"
**43** Secretariat's meal
**44** Fire extinguisher ingredient
**46** Man-mouse connection
**47** El — (weather phenomenon of '98
**48** Comment to Shoeless Joe
**52** Wolfman portrayer Chaney
**53** Cruise film of '81
**54** PDQ
**56** Not for
**59** Singer Garfunkel
**61** Schwarzenegger film of '96
**65** Last name in folk
**66** Beach Boys' cut from "Pet Sounds"
**68** Weapon for Porthos
**69** Pay attention
**70** *Revenge of the —*
**71** Contribute, for a time
**72** Sommer of screen
**73** *Cagney and Lacey* co-star

## Down

**1** Screams at a scarecrow
**2** Drive the getaway car, e.g.
**3** Level the flats
**4** Choral group
**5** Cried like a baby
**6** CPA's busy month
**7** Serling, et al.
**8** Joint presenter
**9** Arrive
**10** Population —
**11** *Star Wars* princess
**12** Partaking
**13** Greasy spoon sign
**18** Classify
**24** Vail forecast
**26** Neuman's magazine
**27** Levi-Strauss specialty
**28** Puccini genre
**29** Eldridge Cleaver's given name
**31** Tearjerker?
**32** Slowpoke
**33** "I can't — satisfaction . . ." (Rolling Stones)
**34** Bean of note
**36** Clinically clean
**41** Miss of Mex.
**42** Flipped item on graduation day
**45** — for words (speechless)
**49** Geronimo, for one
**50** Netanyahu's domain
**51** Henley activity
**55** Group of experts
**56** First victim
**57** Scarf's hangout
**58** Word with pre or ager
**60** Long walk
**62** Dry
**63** Concludes
**64** *Glengarry Glen —*
**67** Keats output

# *Puzzle 1-15: Animal House*

A reference to a foreign country in a clue is crossword code for a foreign language entry as in 46 Down.

## *Across*

1 Rowlands of film
5 "— the ramparts . . ."
8 E.R. term
12 Baseball's Felipe or Moises
13 Go ballistic
14 Baby grand
15 They stick together
18 *Green Eggs and Ham* character
19 Supermarket section
20 Feedbag morsel
21 Burden of proof
23 Scores, in horseshoes
25 Mao —-tung
28 Gin flavoring
30 Penn or Grand Central, for short
31 Letter after theta
33 Affected
35 Campaign word
39 1974 Harry Chapin hit
42 Yarn unit
43 Miss America wear
44 Author Bellow
45 Nile slitherer
47 Have to have
49 *Braveheart* Gibson
50 Diner feature
54 Hit flies
56 Yodeler's perch

57 Neck of the woods
59 *The Rose of —*
63 Chorus girl legwear
66 Navratilova rival
67 "Hey, sailor!"
68 Suffix with smack or sock
69 Prepares the table
70 Stone
71 Loch —

## *Down*

1 Chews the fat
2 Lamb's nom de plume
3 Par
4 Tape introduction
5 Klutz
6 "Golly!"
7 Send to a specialist
8 Take a chair
9 Western resort
10 Lend — (hearken)
11 Civil wrongs
13 *Star Trek* alien
14 Andrew Wyeth, e.g.
16 — *souci*
17 Yalies
22 Out of — (somewhat ill)
24 Big nights
25 Nervous symptoms
26 Enjoy a bath
27 Suffix with cigar or kitchen
29 Allen, e.g.
32 Type of flu
34 Affirmatives
36 Dutch cheese
37 Whodunit board game
38 Archer William
40 Like Sanka
41 Pup's plaything
46 Pop, in Paris
48 Jeanne — (French saint)
50 Cappuccino purveyors
51 Martini garnish
52 Win for the underdog
53 Mark down
55 "Is this seat —?"
58 Arthur of the courts
60 Italian dough
61 Son of Seth
62 Swelled heads
64 McGwire's 70: abbr.
65 Sawyer or Seaver

# Puzzle 1-16: Playing the Symbols

## Across

1 "If I — hammer . . ."
5 Hose problems
10 The Buckeye State
14 — Palme of Sweden
15 Home on high
16 *Alien* abodes
17 She gets what she wants
18 Give the elbow (to)
19 Significant times
20 Clothes horses
23 Skater Babilonia
24 De-crease
25 Celts
28 Verve
29 In one's cups
31 Meat stamp
33 High on Big Ben
34 Hosp. connections
35 Only her hairdresser knows for sure
40 Health watch org.
41 They follow sophs
42 Carol of note
43 Sheep dogs
46 Matched parts
48 Celestial goat
49 "Que —, " (Doris Day tune)
50 Greenlights
53 Non-bubbly bubbly
57 Marseilles milk
59 Handy excuse
60 Collar or circus
61 Peruvian
62 City sound
63 Whirl
64 Mincemeat containers
65 Binge
66 Advantage

## Down

1 *The Planets* composer
2 Molokai bye-bye
3 — Lama
4 From a distance
5 Dee or Bullock
6 Type of brain cell
7 Shakespeare's wood
8 Captain's boats
9 Beholds
10 Offenbach output
11 Leather
12 Gilbert & Sullivan princess

13 CIA precursor
21 Steamed rice dish
22 Big trait for Trump
26 Carpenter's need
27 Bygone campus org.
28 TV time designator
29 Member of the fam.
30 Diamond lady
31 — *the Volcano*
32 Give up at a price
33 Some cars
36 Nabisco's parent
37 — poetica
38 Some pub selections
39 Lotto picks, briefly
40 Half of a dance
44 Burke and Dawn
45 Conductor —-Pekka Salonen
46 Navy member
47 Winter weasel
49 Bake eggs
50 Gaped at
51 Fought dirty
52 Makes tight
54 ITAR-—
55 Bit of film
56 *Hair* hair
57 Sass
58 Cuckoo cousin

# *Puzzle 1-17: Acceleration*

### Across

1 Castle trenches
6 Catches some rays
10 Do a bank job
14 Inuit dwelling
15 Hodgepodge
16 "— bitten, twice shy"
17 First step
20 Eager
21 *Front Page* author Hecht
22 Start
23 *Oliver* tune
25 Miss, with "for"
26 Inmate's out
29 *Speed* setting
30 June 6, 1944
34 Nimble
35 Trading places
37 Sapphic form
38 Proceed with caution
41 ATC point
42 Conductor Koussevitzky
43 Barker, e.g.
44 Pedestal part
46 Tarzan of TV
47 Cavalry weapons
48 Did like Miss Daisy
50 Parlor piece

51 Type of party
54 New currency comm.
55 Barber's specialty
59 Exceed 98.6
62 Italian wine center
63 Stain
64 Cockpit controller
65 Bright fish
66 Faction
67 Wound up

### Down

1 First name of rock
2 Fairy-tale heavy
3 Wings
4 Populace
5 Impresario Hurok
6 In shape
7 King of comedy
8 Zilch
9 First violins, e.g.
10 Ransacked
11 Burden
12 One of the back 40
13 Comfy place
18 Clarinet's cousin
19 Games companion
24 Substitute spreads
25 Cleanse
26 Grabbed at
27 Capital of Guam
28 Got one's goat
29 Like hip-hop togs
31 Musical direction
32 Freud contemporary
33 Sycophant's replies
35 Haggard of songdom
36 Bundle of stalks
39 Uncalled-for
40 Prepare for a fight
45 Make a monk of
47 — grapes
49 Meal lead-in
50 Certain silversides
51 Breakfast staple
52 Wily subterfuge
53 "What's gotten — you?"
54 Like a Kurosawa film
56 Uxmal sight
57 Ruffles feathers
58 Insignificant
60 Larry's buddy
61 Place for the rudder

# Puzzle 1-18: It's About Time

Crosswords favor common verbal utterances that are not necessarily words. (See 48 Across.)

## Across

1 TV clown
5 Yawn
9 — of a Woman (Al Pacino film)
14 Neat as —
15 Hurry, after "step"
16 First part of the Bible
17 Fork division
18 Director Preminger
19 Put on cloud nine
20 Barbra Streisand hit
23 X follower, on TV
24 Switch positions
25 Building extension
28 Workout place
29 Deal makers
33 Keep on a short — (control)
35 Haggard book
36 Very bad
37 Brand-name breakfast quaff
41 Dash
42 — populi
43 Joel Grey Cabaret role
44 "Somewhere over the — . . ."
46 Vise part
48 Disapproving sound
49 Bug
50 — Island, Brooklyn
52 My Left Foot star
58 Helped with the dishes
59 Tuscan river
60 Publisher Condé
61 Florence Nightingale, e.g.
62 City on the Rhine
63 It beats a deuce
64 Vast chasm
65 Peter Pan pirate
66 High point

## Down

1 Belfry inhabitants?
2 Andy's sitcom son
3 Cold-fighting lozenge
4 — a kind (unique)
5 Considerable
6 "The Star Spangled Banner," e.g.
7 Falafel holders
8 School established in 1440
9 Heat source for campers
10 Attraction in Rome
11 Ages
12 "Tiny" Archibald of basketball
13 Café alternative
21 Dawn preceder
22 Distributed, with "out"
25 Fudd of Looney Tunes
26 J.P. Donleavy novel
27 Hawaiian island
29 Tai —
30 Landlord's decision
31 Anne and Jerry
32 Like a cat
34 Positive outlook
35 Clinton's instrument
38 Bring to mind
39 Do a suburban chore
40 Sapphire, e.g.
45 June celebrities
46 Actress Dru or Woodward
47 "Tennis, —?"
50 It holds about 600MB
51 Busybody
52 Defeat decisively
53 Ethereal
54 Places for experiments
55 Enterprise speed
56 Thoughtful reply
57 Underworld river
58 Double helix

# Puzzle 1-19: Pulitzer Prose

## Across

1 Most trivial
6 Geom.
10 Letter carriers' org.
14 Misstep
15 Burn antidote
16 NYSE position
17 Aggressively virile
18 Imposture
19 Heavenly bear
20 1992: Jane Smiley
23 F.A.O. Schwarz purchase
24 Thorn
25 British actress Johns
27 Priestly garb
28 Court
29 Received
30 1939: Marjorie K. Rawlings
35 Alfonso's queen
36 Russo or Clair
37 WWI troops
38 Musial of baseball
39 Everything
40 1979: Sam Shepard
44 Roman 1006
45 Genetic info carrier
46 Lode contents
47 Makes a smooth transition

49 Composer Schifrin
51 Humorist George
54 1994: Edward Albee
57 Gyro bread
58 Pisa's river
59 Narrative work
60 Celt
61 Hawaiian hoedown
62 *Old Possum's Book of Practical Cats* poet
63 Jillian and Miller
64 Make tracks
65 Thick

## Down

1 Paul of *Melvin and Howard*
2 Lyric muse
3 Mehitabel's partner
4 London district
5 Disturb
6 Historian Alfred Thayer
7 Unescorted
8 Insect eater
9 Geometric shape
10 Loan shark's crime
11 Tanzanian plain
12 A book of the saints and martyrs
13 DC's Union, e.g.
21 Island in the Dutch Antilles
22 Dance style
26 Easel
27 Affirmative at sea
28 Sarah, to Abraham
30 Streetcars
31 Swiss
32 Free from ignorance
33 — avis
34 Hawaiian favor
38 Haggard heroine
40 Jane Fonda role in *Klute*
41 Opens
42 Barbie
43 Like the street at rush hour
48 Russian mountain range
49 Porch, in the tropics
50 Spoken
51 Forcefully, to a poet
52 Singer's samples
53 Growing out (of)
55 — Lagoon (diver's mecca)
56 Heraldic border
57 Tiger's tour

# Puzzle 1-20: Two of a Kind

A name that begins with a vowel means instant entry to the Crossword Hall of Fame, as in 24 Across.

## Across

1 Mucho
5 San Antonio cager
9 Denizen of the deep
14 Radiate
15 Skin, as Granny Smith
16 Refuge
17 Grain elevator
18 Elevator man
19 Type of acid
20 Keep pace with
23 Polka —
24 Lennon's lady
25 Snake eyes
27 Grounds
31 Undercover agt.
33 Sentry's command
37 City in western Texas
39 — Speedwagon
40 Part of HOMES
41 Price comparison
44 Bombeck of *At Wit's End*
45 Alley cat
46 Future congers
47 BMOC
48 Caspian feeder
50 Like some fog
51 Pub projectile
53 Chill the Chablis
55 Panhandle
58 Verbatim
64 Normandy beach
66 Breaks the fast
67 Mitch Miller's instrument
68 Hardship
69 Editor's remark
70 Lifelike
71 Cheer up
72 Novelist Paretsky
73 Fontaine role of '44

11 Gung ho
12 Casino city
13 Sea speed
21 Depression
22 Use hieroglyphics
26 Postpone
27 Meant
28 Put on a pedestal
29 Diamond of *Night Court*
30 Nantucket, for one
32 Bouquet
34 "Over the Rainbow" composer
35 Perjurers
36 To the point
38 Conductor Toscanini
42 Garrison
43 Wiser companion
49 Word after weight
52 Mindful
54 — Rica
55 Use a drill
56 Marlene's co-star in *The Blue Angel*
57 Head over heels
59 Computer input
60 Sported
61 Toe the line
62 Crowd sound
63 Opposite of 69 Across
65 Piping —

## Down

1 More or —
2 Leave out
3 Scrabble piece
4 "Knock it off"
5 Table extension?
6 Benefactor
7 *Battle Cry* author
8 Norm Abram of *This Old House*
9 Pentagon, for one
10 Amateur radio licensee

# Puzzle 1-21: Women's Lit.

## Across

1 Ogden of verse
5 Makes the cut
10 Take five
14 Guthrie of folk
15 Inuit boat: var.
16 AOL patron, for one
17 Part of a whole
18 Place for pesetas
19 Check attachment
20 Virginia Woolf book
23 Yoked pair
24 Feather's partner
25 Enters datum
28 Mideastern ruler
30 TV Guide abbr.
33 Some votes
34 "This is only —" (old radio announcement)
35 Ghostly sound
36 Margaret Mitchell book
40 Final onscreen word
41 Sweetens the pot
42 Wise about
43 Legal matter
44 Scorch
45 Annoy
47 Short question?
48 Not worth a red —

49 Ayn Rand book
57 LEM landing spot
58 Computer click-ons
59 Gross
60 Part of A.D.
61 Fortune-teller's deck
62 One of HOMES
63 Word before egg
64 Spun items
65 Takes off

## Down

1 Seaman's abbr.
2 Florence's river
3 Skirt feature
4 Fertile place
5 Kiev cash
6 At full speed
7 Metallic sound
8 Apiece
9 Like Braveheart, e.g.
10 Scuttlebutt
11 Jacob's twin
12 Hairdos
13 Kilmer inspiration
21 Office no.
22 Author Bret
25 Actress Stevens
26 Nary a soul
27 Hangs over
28 Old-fashioned anesthetic
29 Shea Stadium team
30 Wedding gift, perhaps
31 Taboos
32 Fusses
34 "— girl!"
37 "It — big deal" (forget it)
38 Favoritism, e.g.
39 More deserving
45 Bank jobs?
46 Abby's twin sister
47 Beginning of Primo Levi title
48 Type of contrapuntal music
49 Gov. agent
50 Fine-tune
51 Very long time
52 Sports org.
53 Unit of pressure
54 Pale shade
55 Related to
56 Uses henna

# Puzzle 1-22: Playing the Numbers

A "starter" in a clue is crossword code for prefix, and has nothing to do with eating! (See 63 Across.)

## Across

1 Compos mentis
5 Hoosegow
9 Branches
13 Stopper
14 Arterial beat
15 Pout
16 First followers
19 "Live free or —" (NH motto)
20 Prod
21 *The Age of Anxiety* poet
22 Eye amorously
23 Coop group
25 Second followers
32 Sour-tasting
33 Nautical cry
34 French law
35 Hurl
36 Kind of exam
38 Sportscaster Albert
39 Language suffix
40 Cry from the sty
41 Buddhist's destiny
42 Third followers
46 Collar type
47 Lotion ingredient
48 *Giant* ranch
51 State of pique
52 "Mighty — a Rose"
55 Fourth followers
59 Daytime TV staple
60 Take — for the worse
61 Satanic
62 Acts human
63 Dose or cycle starter
64 Arctic native

## Down

1 Nail
2 Et —
3 Artist's model
4 Gamete
5 Supreme Court members
6 Not aweather
7 "No man — hero to his valet"
8 Author Deighton
9 Surprise attack
10 The Beatles' "Abbey —"
11 Erato, e.g.
12 Spotted
14 "Ici on — francais"
17 British sort
18 Fine's partner
22 Bettor's concern
23 Sunken fence
24 Organic compound
25 Hose down
26 Twenty combiner
27 Second-generation Japanese-American
28 Some armored vehicles
29 A.M. rouser
30 Bellini opera
31 Parlor piece
36 Greek dough
37 Quickly, with "instant"
38 Concocted
40 Based on eight
41 Stomach problems
43 Diminishments
44 Supreme Court Justice Day O'Connor
45 Sigourney Weaver thriller
48 Stood up
49 — effort
50 Open a bit
51 Cozy
52 Etna output
53 "Take — from me . . ."
54 Iodine source
56 Sweet potato
57 Gulped down
58 — Aviv

# Puzzle 1-23: Name Game

A question mark at the end of a clue tips you off to wordplay.

### Across

1 "— the Goldrush" (Neil Young)
6 Inventor Howe
11 It can be a gift
14 Motivation
15 Ling-Ling, e.g.
16 — de Janeiro
17 Dragged a Revolutionary War hero?
19 Woodworking tool
20 Expenditure
21 Crone
22 — facto
23 LPs replacements
24 TV star Gulager
26 Caroline, to Ted Kennedy
28 Hurled brickbats at *Nixon* director?
32 Where "land-ho" is shouted from
35 *Delta of Venus* author Anais
36 Sarcastic
37 Hammett hound
38 Plaster painting
41 Town outside Tulsa
42 Gaucho's lariat
44 Hither and —
45 Erects, with "up"
46 Trapped *Moonstruck* actor?
50 Doom's companion
51 Kith's companion

52 Avg.
55 "Rat Pack" member Bishop
57 Evian or Vichy
59 More inquisitive
61 Henley participant
62 Walloped an American poet?
64 Nice summer
65 Edible tubers
66 Type of board
67 Timothy Leary's letters
68 Wasted
69 Every story has two

### Down

1 Impromptu
2 Charlatan
3 Pinball machine mistakes
4 First name in daredevils
5 Prepare for publication
6 DC group est. in '70
7 Strip of wood
8 Under control
9 Musical tempo
10 — Diego
11 "I heard it through the —"
12 Helps out
13 Old-time TV clown
18 Hose
22 Remote air
25 Unicorn fish
27 U.S. Open champ Ernie
28 Dignified
29 Pop. reference
30 See 5 Down
31 World Series winners of 1975-1976
32 Painter Chagall
33 Where most people live
34 Thrown for a loop
39 Falsify financial records
40 Place to surf
43 Fuss
47 "Forget it!"
48 Contaminated
49 Battery terminals
52 Assessed, with "up"
53 — Haute, IN
54 Carts
55 "The Piano Man" man
56 Dobbin's meal
58 Later
60 H'way rig
62 There are two in a qt.
63 It ends in Oct.

# Puzzle 1-24: Applause

## Across

1 Nonsense
5 Bitter
10 Lives in a book?
14 Code of note
15 Quaker pronoun
16 Singular performance
17 Glance over
18 Most attractive
20 Girl Scout's guide
22 Overturn
23 Takes off
24 *Swan Lake* wear
26 Stick to
29 From scratch
33 Equal
34 Book leaf
35 Veneto, e.g.
36 Difficulties
37 Basketball center
38 Night sound
39 Sault — Marie
40 *Home Improvement* star Tim
41 Helper
42 Game using a wall
44 Meander
46 On the — (not speaking)
47 Obey
48 Barely
51 Golfer's concern
55 Acrobatic feat
58 Fitzgerald of song
59 Funny Johnson
60 Murphy of *The Unforgiven*
61 *Anna and the King of* —
62 Grandpa Walton
63 In good — (advantage)
64 Lots

## Down

1 Wild time
2 Whale of a film?
3 Connery or Penn
4 Tamers, e.g.
5 "Make yourself —"
6 Confusion
7 Skater's milieu
8 Neither Rep. Nor Dem.
9 — Moines
10 Beads for cash
11 Mine finds
12 Sun follower

13 Dillon of *Gunsmoke*
19 Achieve a personal best
21 Exclude
24 Eagle claw
25 Single measure
26 Like a monkey
27 Gamma follower
28 Hayes of stage
29 Shanty
30 Steer clear of
31 Electronic device with two terminals
32 ". . . purple people — . . ."
34 Satiates
37 Land plan
38 Most convenient
40 Borders
43 One of Rudolph's crew
44 Like an eagle
45 Common connection
47 "Beatle—"
48 Type of rug
49 Day — center
50 Poker stake
51 Pelt
52 Madison Ave. award
53 King of comedy
54 Dawber and namesakes
56 — de deux
57 Monotonous routine

# Puzzle 1-25: Ready, Set . . .

Beware of surnames that double as proper nouns — as in 61 Across.

## Across

1 Kid around
5 Snapshot
10 Pepper, et al.
14 Elbow neighbor
15 Put in a bigger engine
16 Roll of stamps
17 Actress Patricia *(Hud)*
18 "Goodnight, —" (popular tune by Lead Belly)
19 *The Man — Mancha*
20 "Laugh-In" entertainer
22 Designer Cassini
23 —-force wind
24 Award presented by Chris Berman
26 Called the doctor?
29 Atlantis, e.g.
31 Clio winners
34 Age of note
35 Genesis opener
37 Carson of the frontier
38 Permit
39 Greenlight
40 *— Got a Secret*
41 The Plastic — Band
42 Deed holders
43 "—, in the name of love . . ."
44 Gregory Hines' forte
45 Like Pegasus
46 Twosomes

47 Man or Wight
49 Bartlett, e.g.
51 Keep, in proofreading lingo
53 Try one's hardest
59 *Puttin' on the Ritz* group
60 Sizing made from egg white
61 Pound of poetry
62 Team players?
63 Beethoven dedicatee
64 *London Fields* author Martin
65 Beyond one's years
66 Drew a line in the sand
67 "He who laughs — . . ."

## Down

1 Freud contemporary
2 Ersatz butter
3 Hose problem
4 Type of headlight
5 Pharmacist's bottle
6 Singer Lena
7 Mideast cartel
8 *Name That —*
9 Some Gilbert & Sullivan works
10 Journalist's pursuit
11 "Take a hike!"
12 Mah-jongg piece
13 Foundry residue
21 Dear old —
25 Wearing Wellies
26 Type of light
27 Arco of Sacramento
28 Lose it
29 *Politically Incorrect* host
30 North Sea feeder
32 Tiger Woods' mark
33 *The 39 —* (Alfred Hitchcock film)
35 Like many a wrangler
36 Sweater girl Turner
39 World Cup score
43 Like Dali's work
46 Type of flatfish
48 Actress Sharon
49 Savoir faire
50 Blew it
51 Tuck away
52 Old TV sitcom
54 Pueblo pot
55 *Vanity —*
56 Baum princess
57 Actor Kristofferson
58 — *of Eden*

# Puzzle 1-26: Step into the Sixties

**HINT**

Another clue for 62 Down is "French fashion magazine."

## Across

1 "The drinks are —!"
5 — Crunch (kiddie cereal)
9 Chalky
14 Slippery item
15 Toast topper
16 Remove the stubble
17 Plastic bags go-with
19 — of Hoffman
20 Dog catcher's catch
21 Roll call reply, Cockney style
22 Cast out
23 Word with safety
25 Jeanne — (French saint)
27 Tarzan, et al.
31 Did a plumber's job
35 Carpentry groove
36 Lawn mower's path
40 Took a taxi
41 Ken of *thirtysomething*
42 Landlord's sign
43 Senate aide
44 *To Kill a Mockingbird* star Gregory
45 Part of ICBM
46 Jack of old oaters
47 — *the Truth* (old-time TV show)
49 Sacrificial sites
51 River to the Bay of Korea
53 "So long"
54 Horseshoe and soft-shell
57 Country club type
59 Shopaholic's treat
64 Moroccan capital
65 Barbie doll hairdos
67 "I want — just like . . ."
68 Fencing weapon
69 Pretzel coating
70 Betsy — (Tiny Tears contemporary)
71 Warren Beatty film
72 Iditarod vehicle

## Down

1 Chooses
2 Gingrich, to friends
3 Golda of Israel
4 Big cat of film
5 Fold-away furniture
6 Sci-fi visitor
7 Use a spyglass
8 Snooped
9 Nautical term
10 Hairy hardwood cover
11 —-Bopp (comet)
12 Arden and namesakes
13 Hornet's home
18 Use an Underwood
24 Endow
26 Restaurant souvenir
27 Vote to accept
28 Prefix meaning "*prehistoric*"
29 King's proclamation
30 Playground structure
32 Aussie native
33 Poe's first name
34 Considers
37 Took the gold
38 PC key
39 Shirt shape
48 In conclusion
50 "— we forget . . ."
52 Word with case
53 Filleted
54 Stick in one's — (fester)
55 Throw a tantrum
56 Slightly
58 You can skip it
60 Fail's opposite
61 Iranian currency
62 First name in supermodeling
63 Some tax returns, for short
66 Word of acceptance

# Puzzle 1-27: What's Cooking?

Crosswords are always G-rated, peppered by a few repeaters that fall into the category of "Mild expletive," as in 4 Down.

## Across

1 *Fall of the House of —*
6 Region
10 Official records
14 Attack
15 Hideouts
16 In bed, with "up"
17 Anglo-Saxon date
18 Hops kiln
19 Economist Smith
20 French dish
22 Richard of screen
23 Refusenik's word
24 Kilt pattern
26 Big bunch
30 In need of Jenny Craig
32 Short visit
33 King of Israel
35 Resell tickets at a profit
39 Anastasia's ancestor
41 *She Stoops to —*
43 Madrid mister
44 Chicken — (recipe)
46 Goad
47 Taunting one
49 Perturbed
51 Travolta musical
54 Civil rights grp.

56 Check
57 Italian dish
63 Actor Ray
64 Melange
65 Enraged
66 "Where's the —?"
67 Essence
68 Bell town
69 Slave of old
70 See 69A
71 Swiss cheese features

## Down

1 Leatherneck grp.
2 Place for a missile
3 — apparent
4 "Good grief!"
5 Face-lifted
6 Sun-dried brick
7 House seller
8 Word in the Massachusetts motto
9 Shrewd
10 Like a Spartan dish
11 West Pointer
12 Gala gear
13 Hype producers
21 Hose material
25 Part of PGA
26 Caresses
27 Church area
28 Bridge
29 Russian dish
31 Aqua
34 Build
36 Presence
37 Drumsticks
38 Quarry
40 Author Murdoch
42 Rudimentary seed
45 Shiraz native
48 Suit
50 East Indian watercourse
51 Snatches
52 Top leader of the Grays
53 **Downy** duck
55 $100 bill
58 Pints at the pub
59 Venetian beach
60 Ellipse
61 Number of Muses
62 Vows

# Puzzle 1-28: Dem Joints

A question mark at the end of a clue indicates wordplay.

## Across

1 Mortify
6 Get it
11 Cool — cucumber
14 *The Iliad* and *The Odyssey*
15 Musical beats
16 Opp. SSE
17 Unique slow pitch
19 Barbie's beau
20 Sounds like a lake
21 Need for a Kleenex?
23 Latin I word
25 Anoint
26 Dietary no-no
29 11 has two
31 Rendezvous
34 Numerical suffix
35 Stable areas
37 Coward of stage
38 Go for another term
40 Worthless French coin
41 Sports org.
42 First word, often
43 Gaudy
46 Dutch carrier
47 Consume, in a way
49 Sub, sometimes
50 Recruiting letters
51 Cove
53 Hit signs
55 Shows compassion
58 Type of flu
61 Connector
62 Court figure's complaint
65 66, e.g.
66 Subject for Kafka
67 Grooves
68 Bagel go-with
69 Missouri American Indian
70 Winter Palace residents

## Down

1 Query
2 Source of ruin
3 Malarial fever
4 Musica —
5 Husky owners
6 Tel. company
7 CSA soldiers
8 Town in Iowa
9 Bone supports
10 Purloin
11 They go with sneakers
12 Snicker—
13 Bristles
18 Not upright
22 Errol of swashbuckling
24 Dangle a carrot
26 Physicist Enrico
27 Mr. T's series, after *The*
28 Dictionary feature
30 Wet sound
32 Ducks
33 Some are grand
36 Pear-shaped instrument
39 Aches and —
43 Antennae
44 Wall hanging
45 Most relaxed
48 Out of it
52 Tapeworm genus: var.
54 Sedimentary deposits
55 *Nova* host Sagan
56 Wise about
57 Hitch
59 Magician's opening
60 Bete —
63 Seine sight
64 "There once — a girl . . ."

# Puzzle 1-29: Bank-ability

HINT

Look at the title carefully while unraveling the theme for this puzzle.

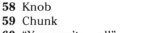

## Across

1 Radiance
5 Tree fern of N.Z.
10 Broom closet stuff
14 Tool about
15 Eiger gear
16 Cut and paste
17 Gets wiser, perhaps
18 Video game maker
19 Broadway prize
20 They deal in futures?
23 Bad mood
24 Tai people
25 You chew these
28 Grids
33 Bank queue?
35 Hawaiian greeting
36 Summed, with "up"
37 Blue ribbon position
38 On foot, Parisian style
40 Long limb
41 What non-prime borrowers get?
43 Dear
46 Black Sea port
47 Grade school trio
48 Indigo plant

49 Uncool savings plans?
56 Oz penner Frank
57 University of Maine town
58 Knob
59 Chunk
60 "You can't — all"
61 Neutral shade
62 Heels
63 Tournament rankings
64 It holds things together

## Down

1 Wimbledon winner
2 Trademark
3 Done
4 Bernstein opus — *Story*
5 Victor Borge, e.g.
6 Chamber music composition
7 — as a pin
8 Station, in Paris
9 It's the pits
10 Shooting star
11 Bouquet
12 Safety and bobby
13 Pig's place
21 Pressed backspace
22 Jet —
25 It's at the top
26 Law's partner
27 Shelf
28 Part of CD's
29 Division word
30 Often assumed item
31 Joins up
32 Cassette option
34 Stead
38 "Ciao" alternative
39 Chopin works
41 *The — of Werther* (Goethe)
42 Cpls.
44 Hansel and Gretel trail mix
45 401(k) kin
48 Spotty
49 Room at the casa
50 Campus loc.
51 Perry victory site
52 Better than OK
53 Pleasant
54 Scarlett's home
55 Urban blight
56 Univ. degree

# Puzzle 1-30: Home Teams

Roman numerals are a nifty way of stringing together unlikely consonants, as in 8 Down.

## Across

1 Butte's kin
5 Enthusiasm
10 Zoo transport, in San Diego
14 Word on a door
15 Benefit
16 Turtle's running rival
17 Larval oyster
18 Land of the 49ers
20 From scratch
22 Gas —
23 One of a pair
24 Flushing field
26 Tick away
29 Hardy folk
33 Land of the Fighting Sioux
35 Caviar
36 E, W, N, and S
37 Accomplished
38 Unskilled helper
39 Failed amendment
40 Where the Rams roam
44 Throws in the towel
46 Tight ties
47 City of Yemen
48 ER term
49 He taught Stradivari
52 Hems
56 Land of the Huskies
59 Matinee —
60 Type of sax
61 Empty
62 Hot Roman fiddler?
63 Endorsements
64 Enticed
65 Nibble, rodent-style

## Down

1 Entwine
2 Montreal exhibition of '67
3 *King and I* setting
4 Tries
5 Packed up
6 Sidestep
7 Death rattle
8 Seven on a sun dial
9 Santa's helper
10 Blackmail, e.g.
11 *Atlas Shrugged* author Ayn
12 "La donna e mobile," e.g.
13 Square —
19 "Rigoletto," e.g.

21 Bangers' go-with
24 Fine china label
25 Bowler, for one
26 Came to a conclusion
27 Longest French flower
28 Wall tapestry
29 On the — (ruined)
30 Neighborhoods
31 Hermit Herman
32 Forwards e-mail
34 Decorate
38 Conspiratorial
40 Line segments
41 "Giddyup!"
42 Chanted
43 Make like a hawk
45 Sympathetic pity
48 Reflected
49 Absent
50 A sex
51 Charles' family pet
52 Main role player
53 Paradise
54 Screenwriter Ephron
55 Like a snail
57 Zilch
58 Wildebeest

# Puzzle 1-31: Northern Exposure

Old-time TV is eternally in reruns in puzzles, as you can see from the reference to Imogene Coca in 18 Across.

## Across

1 Feed a party
6 "— Rosenkavalier"
9 Trim the roast
14 Mad Hatter's guest
15 "Sweet as apple cider" girl
16 Answering machine button
17 Eddie Rickenbacker, for one
18 Imogene's partner in comedy
19 Cut at a 45-degree angle
20 Adam's madam
21 Spitsbergen locale
24 Singer Neil
26 Shortly
27 Yanks opponents
29 Artist LeRoy
34 Shrinking inland sea
37 Rorschach test image
40 Booby trap
41 Iditarod haulers
44 1988 Oscar winner Kevin
45 Remove, with "off"
46 Part of MIT
47 Place for an ace
49 Suffix with leather or disk
51 Airline to Jerusalem
54 Least known
58 Mars phenomenon

63 Alt. spelling
64 "Say cheese" reaction
65 Popular card game
66 *J'accuse* author Zola
68 "— Doll" (old-time song)
69 Draw
70 Moth-eaten
71 Pick up the tab
72 Pass catcher
73 Collar inserts

## Down

1 Cloaks
2 Energetic
3 Like a mosaic
4 Earth-friendly prefix
5 Second try
6 Thing to spin
7 Uses a blue pencil
8 Ham's medium
9 She-devil
10 Clapton of rock
11 Destiny
12 On the bounding main
13 Gull relation
22 Talmudic teacher
23 One in the clink
25 *What's My Line* panelist Francis
28 Affront
30 Less moonlit
31 Sinclair Lewis street
32 Greek war god
33 Bird's — soup
34 Makes inquiries
35 Brooklet
36 Rose's admirer
38 Small bill
39 Quaker pronoun
42 Deeply respectful
43 Marine or violet starter
48 Inventor Whitney
50 Candles
52 Perceptive
53 Bolshevism founder
55 Role for Madonna
56 Like seawater
57 Deuce beaters
58 "Hey, you!"
59 Sharif of screen
60 Lo-cal
61 Inter — (among others)
62 Type of team, for short
67 Place to wrestle

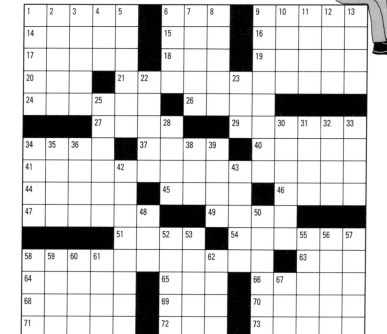

# Puzzle 1-32: B List

## Across

1 Lures
6 Stalk
10 Basics
14 Tunesmiths' org.
15 On-screen screen
16 "Are you for —?"
17 Body clock, e.g.
19 — *La Douce*
20 Juan lead-in
21 Dr. Westheimer
22 Mickey Mouse creator Walt
24 Inuit settlement in Greenland
25 Kinda
26 Type of barron
29 Occasional
32 In the lead
33 Full of — (in high spirits)
34 Guido's note
35 Author E.J.
36 Type of suit
37 Traffic sign
38 Women's lib lost cause
39 Pulitzer —
40 Dom DeLuise role
41 Irish patriot
43 Stagger
44 Greek epic, with "The"
45 "If I — hammer . . ."
46 In-between leader
48 Medicinal amount
49 Feel poorly
52 One in a million
53 French general
56 Gen. Bradley
57 *Penny* — (The Beatles)
58 Forest obscurers
59 Chums
60 Piccadilly figure
61 Overweight

## Down

1 Barbara, familiarly
2 Minor continent
3 Screen click-on
4 Indian cymbals
5 Wore
6 Patti of rock
7 Part of MIT
8 Spanish queen
9 *Car 54* officer, et al.
10 Honor society
11 Actress Peters
12 Arrived
13 Do in the dragon
18 Type of gum
23 Some sale tags
24 Israeli statesman Abba
25 Outpouring
26 Cleared the lawn
27 Chicago hub
28 Type of psychology
29 Without, Italian style
30 "You win" implication
31 Type of chicken
33 Big name in marionettes
36 Introduction
37 Mrs. Roosevelt
39 Ballet move
40 Filmmaker's technique, with "black"
42 Changes
43 House in Havana
45 Sharpens
46 Shore, with "up"
47 Incarnation of Vishnu
48 Ursula Andress film
49 Suit to —
50 Followers
51 — majeste
54 Item on loan?
55 Planet

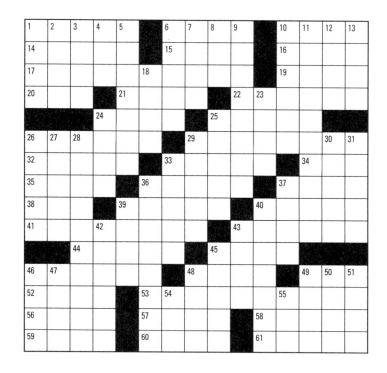

# Puzzle 1-33: Fish Stories

Flightless birds of the ratite family belong to the lexicon of crossword repeaters. (See 2 Down.)

### Across

1 Give off
5 Ghanaian language
9 1984 film — *Man*
13 Like Nancy Sinatra's boots?
15 Pindaric verse
17 Cousteau study groups?
18 La Traviata composer
19 Mail
20 Power grabber
22 German city
25 Skeptical remark
27 White House Al
28 Fabled birds
29 Driving hazard
30 Hindu princess
32 Med. course
33 Fledermaus
34 Carol starter
37 — *vous plait*
38 Bad forecast at the shore?
40 Velvet ender
41 Bakery treat
43 Chang's other half
44 *Hair* hair
45 Science magazine
46 Heading

47 Knitting direction
48 Fido's choice
50 Never, with "time"
52 Something to cop
53 Operatic voice
55 Unescorted
57 Patois
58 Suspected, at sea?
63 Uptight
64 Double agent?
65 Glitzy light
66 Court proceedings
67 Trick finisher

### Down

1 Road curve
2 Kiwi's cousin
3 Under the weather
4 Teapot event
5 Summer acquisitions
6 Quiescent
7 LBJ pet
8 Publish
9 Déjà vu, again?
10 Table piece
11 Intentional at the shore?
12 More peculiar
14 It waxes and wanes
16 Hibernia
21 "— Days" (the Doors)
22 Wipe out
23 Boom introduction
24 Veal-fish dish?
26 — you and me . . .
29 European peninsula
31 Tally
35 French earth
36 — Gay
38 German article
39 Fresh
42 Gentle: mus.
44 Materializes
48 — were (so to speak)
49 Type of coat
51 Cavaradossi's love
52 Pay to play
54 So be it
56 Gymnast Korbut
59 Small shoe?
60 Queue after Q
61 Copy
62 Ares gone Norse

# Puzzle 1-34: Hidden Assets

A reference to a foreign country in a clue calls for an entry in the native tongue of that country.

## Across

1 Parisienne's headwear
6 Civil rights org.
10 Shadow
14 Not — in the world
15 Bridge
16 Bread spread
17 "Ring of Fire" singer
19 Hefty slice
20 Response to a ques.
21 Petits —
22 Consumed amount
24 Leslie Caron classic
25 Social starter
26 Morro Castle city
29 Late-night quaff
33 Eastern chieftains
34 Sally in space
35 Connector
36 Like cheeks in winter
37 Skin and —
38 Scott Turow title
39 Ballerina's dress
40 "Rock of —"
41 Clown booster
42 Rubouts
44 Combines, with "together"
45 Charles or Camilla
46 Weeds
47 Skillful
50 Composes
51 — de cologne
54 Yoko's son
55 Buys too much
58 Tangy
59 Cleo's domain
60 Sure competitor
61 Seed covers
62 Nights before
63 Hot hangout

12 News breach
13 Ear piece?
18 Eastern discipline
23 Advanced degree
24 "Quarter to Three" singer
25 Staff
26 *Ah Sin* co-author
27 Love, on the Riviera
28 Horizon
29 Dress to the —
30 Like a dunce's cap
31 Fred's sister
32 Hits with snowballs
34 Thesaurus man
37 Low voice
41 Costa Rican catnaps
43 Mr. Geller
44 Singer Lily
46 "— Johnny!"
47 Urgent letters
48 Art —
49 Attack
50 Soccer great
51 Nearly beige
52 Like, sort of
53 Gov. agency
56 Lucy's co-star, familiarly
57 "Are you a man — mouse?"

## Down

1 California peninsula
2 Bus. major's course
3 Cheers
4 Sea bird
5 Alley game
6 Code standard for computers
7 April 15 VIPs
8 — Vegas
9 Maddens
10 Stickums
11 — breve: mus.

# Puzzle 1-35: Code Names

## Across

1 Kind of trip
4 "There is nothing like —" (South Pacific)
9 Mets' home
13 Get — deal (lose out)
14 Composer Franz
15 Bottom of the barrel
16 LE
19 Amor attachment
20 "Imagine me and — . . ."
21 Active start
22 Intrinsically
24 Valerie Harper role
26 Type of fever ?
29 Corner
30 Kind of flakes
31 Prevalent
32 Pequod's co-owner
34 Defeated
36 LN
39 Eat
40 Slander
41 Layer
42 Lap dog, for short
43 *Good Times* actor John —
47 Hostelry
48 Skip over
50 Stationary

51 Musical Bobby
53 Type of blanket
55 Pedro's uncle
56 RT
60 Sty cry
61 Jagged
62 Like the TV ranger
63 Porgy's beloved
64 Unusual
65 Seraglio chamber

## Down

1 Pencil end
2 James Bond girl Pussy —
3 Hooter
4 In addition
5 One who objects
6 "I get it!"
7 — of Honor (wedding attendant)
8 Went astray
9 Box
10 Japanese emperor
11 List ender
12 — Wednesday
13 Take as one's own
17 Sailor's reply
18 Call — day (retire)
23 Musical group
25 Worked on the price
27 — *Good Men*
28 Desire
30 Stain
31 Type of sleeve
33 Hearing aids?
34 Mrs. Bill Paley
35 Chin end
36 Before long
37 Kampala natives
38 Same here
39 *"— on parle francais"*
42 *The Second Mrs. Tanqueray* dramatist
44 System
45 Journalist Fallaci
46 Little Eva's creator
48 *"— tu . . ."* (Verdi aria)
49 Napery
50 Big Board initials
52 Clumsy crafts
54 Dusseldorf donkey
56 Where to find corn
57 Tell a whopper
58 *"Mazel —!"*
59 Co. in N. Ireland

# Puzzle 1-36: Brain Power

In crossword code, the word "short" in a clue indicates an abbreviation in the entry. (See 32 Across.)

## Across

1 Work units
5 "Ta-ta!"
8 Terrycloth item
13 Dynamic beginning
14 Persia, nowadays
15 Popeye's honey
16 Bankbook replacement, perhaps
18 Pine product
19 Walk softly
20 Strike out, as text
22 Ernie of golf
23 Frat letters
25 Backs
27 Impressionist Edgar
29 World Cup game
32 Short tummy muscles?
35 Least
37 River to the Ligurian Sea
38 — to New Castle
40 Old-time actress Joanne
41 Worries
42 Roman robe
43 — d' (host)
45 "Mayday!"
46 Wonder of song
48 Nose nipper Jack
50 Trite
52 Impose a tax
55 Puzzle clue tag
57 Half hitch, e.g.
59 Salt of auric acid
61 Display, as charm
63 Perceptive
65 Tread
66 Hard to handle
67 Trig ratio
68 *Angela's* — (Frank McCourt best-seller)
69 Extra man in the ring
70 Like — of bricks

## Down

1 Part of SEATO
2 Send in money
3 Bar chart, e.g.
4 Worked on the laundry
5 Piece of a two-piece
6 Gridiron division
7 Wrapped up
8 Corrida celeb
9 Corrida cheer
10 Know-it-alls
11 Diabolical
12 Camera — cap
14 Frigid time of yore
17 American Indian poles
21 In need of direction
24 Common bonitos
26 Surgery reminder
28 Letter embellishment
30 Word form for "within"
31 Supreme Diana
32 Plays a part
33 Italy's shape
34 Western shrub
36 *Kama* —
39 Fuji flow
41 Come clean
43 Stingy
44 Prayer beads
47 Printing plant pots
49 Mother —
51 Failure
53 "— with flowers"
54 Court figure
55 Miles of *Psycho*
56 Allies' foe
58 "Of — I sing"
60 Shangri-la
62 Barely passing grade
64 Politico Landon

# Puzzle 1-37: I'll Take Manhattan

**57** Downtown Manhattan landmark
**63** Catch of the day, perhaps
**64** Borden's bull
**65** Fashion read
**67** Travel mode
**68** Put on cloud nine
**69** First name in country
**70** Lecherous look
**71** Café cup
**72** 2000, e.g.

## Down

**1** Passing mark
**2** Detriment
**3** Atlas section
**4** *Foucault's* — (Umberto Eco book)
**5** Nacho go-with
**6** Baseball bird
**7** *Huckleberry* —
**8** Riding the waves
**9** Tennis term
**10** Malayan island
**11** Abraham's grandson
**12** — quam videri (North Carolina motto)
**13** Astaire's step
**21** Goodnight girl
**22** Mind-reader's letters
**25** Breakfast choice
**26** Spit and —
**27** Element #5
**29** Pigeon's perch
**30** Med. test
**32** Tie go-with
**33** Bolivia's constitutional capital
**34** Keyboard key
**36** AMC alternative
**38** Venomous one
**41** Sailor
**42** Miss America topper
**43** Tulsa plant
**48** Scribble
**49** Cul-de-—
**51** Aspects
**54** Trapshooting
**56** Babe Ruth's number
**57** Kind of rug
**58** Gate opener
**59** First name in scat
**60** Short holiday?
**61** Word with club
**62** Isolated isle
**63** Sellout sign
**66** Musical aptitude

## Across

**1** Bloke
**5** Roll-aways
**10** Shade of red
**14** Facility
**15** Crop up
**16** Mountain in Thessaly
**17** Actress Moran
**18** Ocean —
**19** Smithy's tool
**20** Uptown Manhattan address
**23** Caspian Sea feeder
**24** Computer add-on
**25** Best-selling book
**28** *Nightmare on — Street*
**31** Oater group
**35** Become, with "to"
**37** Victorian, e.g.
**39** Attila the —
**40** Midtown Manhattan neighborhood
**44** Type of trip
**45** Schoolyard game
**46** Capital on the Missouri
**47** Imparts
**50** Man with a whistle
**52** Chasing
**53** Western alliance: abbr.
**55** Longfellow's bell town

# Puzzle 1-38: Every Which Way

Beware of surnames that double as parts of speech, as in 70 Across.

## Across

1 Schmooze
4 Make a break for it
8 Elbow
13 Fuss
14 Order at Starbucks
16 Presided (over)
17 Tolstoy
18 Protégé
20 Type of sock
22 Den
23 Spoil, with "upon"
24 Where Lipinski shines
26 Wear and —
28 Jilted
34 Start of N.H. motto
35 Director Spike
36 Type of board
37 Friend, for Francois
38 Shows up
41 Ready-fire go-between
42 Girder
44 Chanoyu ritual drink
45 Start the game
46 Blue
50 Something fishy?
51 Fleuret's kin
52 Obstacle
55 Quantrill's action
58 Create law
61 In perfect condition
64 "Pretty maids all in a —"
65 Sat in neutral
66 King of Judea
67 Actor Wallach
68 Afrikaners
69 Japanese coins
70 Rather, news-wise

## Down

1 Jubilee
2 Arabian gulf
3 Newspaper stand-by
4 Flowing
5 Sitting position
6 Common catch-all
7 Enceladus' burial place
8 Theater sign
9 Boring
10 Spicy stew
11 Jacket feature
12 *The Razor's* — (Somerset Maugham)

19 Native Canadian
21 The longest sentence
25 Braveheart's garb
27 Pint fillers
28 Back-breaking dance
29 Surf site
30 Sink one's — into
31 Showed up again
32 Makes oneself heard
33 Sunday song
34 In bed, with "up"
38 Surrounded by
39 Wedding page word
40 Miami's county
43 "If it's not one thing, it's —"
45 Peck film, after "The"
47 Mrs. Nick Charles
48 Warhol film
49 Turns over
52 Rugrat's place
53 Venetian resort
54 Make eyes at
56 Ruffles feathers
57 Throw down the gauntlet
59 Soda selection
60 Abby or Ann
62 QB's concerns
63 Charged particle

# Puzzle 1-39: Lost in New York

## Across

1 Spear
5 Chops down
10 "Goldberg Variations" composer
14 Duffer's target
15 In a row
16 Pan's love
17 From a distance
18 Jungle vine
19 Quod follower
20 Popular harmony quartet?
23 Ball prop
24 "Give — rest!"
25 First —
28 James of jazz
31 Late-night meal
36 Exult
38 Spare —
40 Snare
41 Beautiful woman of legend?
44 Calendario starter
45 "Heads up!"
46 Iron and bauxite
47 Passover meals
49 Aerie
51 Vane direction
52 Place for a half nelson
54 Steeped drink
56 Wild West showman?

64 Herr's mate
65 Thrill
66 Double-reed instrument
67 Poke fun at
68 Tennis star Monica
69 Watercourse
70 Don Juan's mom
71 Puts on the frills
72 Jodie Foster film of '94

## Down

1 O'Neal, to pals
2 Veggie staple
3 Mercury's wings
4 Henri's cap
5 Frankie Valli's voice, e.g.
6 Door sign
7 Role for Jim Carrey
8 Hawaiian spot
9 Leans
10 Grievance
11 Section section
12 Scorch
13 Fenced goods, e.g.
21 Maiden name introducer
22 It makes you sweat
25 They go before pains
26 Dunne of film
27 Handled out
29 Misunderstanding
30 Match play?
32 Country rock group
33 Spews out
34 Nagano curves
35 Ex-Dodger
37 *The Way We —*
39 Fictional Jane
42 Marilyn's given name
43 Unable to sit still
48 Most lucid
50 — Aviv
53 Author Anne
55 Early oak
56 Island off Ireland
57 Dilly-dally
58 Marine haircut
59 "Jewel of the East"
60 Scoop
61 Tony's cousin
62 Barbie, e.g.
63 Holler
64 Part of TGIF

# Puzzle 1-40: Name Game

Volcanos have made their presence felt in puzzle repeaters, as in 57 Down.

## Across

1 Bog fuel
5 Chalcedony
10 Voracious
14 Ticklish Muppet
15 Light lunch
16 Vegas game
17 Pilaf for a playwright?
19 Daily supplement
20 Showy bloomers
21 "— meat is another . . ."
23 Cape near Boston
24 Slow boats
25 Picasso, et al.
29 Rebounded
32 Pulitzer winner
33 Author Bret
35 — *Got a Secret*
36 Charitable contribution
37 Hiawatha's craft
38 Singer Campbell
39 Eye action, for short
40 Totes
41 "— we all!"
42 Spot for babes
44 Cruel people
46 Madonna's ex
47 Cast out
48 Oscar winner of '98
51 I specialists
55 "Son of —!"
56 Flower for a showman?
58 Sound quality
59 Coral island
60 Arab sultanate
61 Fed up with
62 Tenant's protection
63 Oddball

## Down

1 Chick's remark
2 Vogue rival
3 Arsenal contents
4 Place for polish
5 Sanction
6 Long-snouted fish
7 Actress MacGraw
8 Mexican meal
9 Toothless
10 Arms position
11 Distance for an actress?
12 Privy to
13 Dresses
18 Henna, e.g.
22 Seine feeder
25 Isolated
26 Logger's match
27 Choreographer's choice?
28 Pottery fragment
29 Traverse
30 Happening
31 Fender benders
34 Rocker Adam
37 Man-eater
38 Football field
40 Actor James
41 Amigo sign-off
43 Derived support, with "on"
45 Sock pattern
48 Funny Frenchman Jacques
49 Stravinsky
50 Refer to
51 Type of pipes
52 A handful
53 Despot of yore
54 Thrill
57 Mauna —

# Puzzle 1-41: Store Signs, for Starters

HINT

"Starters," as used in the title, is crossword code for "prefixes."

## Across

1 Went lickety-split
5 Take five
9 Director's nightmare
13 Big cat
15 Mob kingpin
16 Andy Taylor's kid
17 Prime time for hunters
19 Siberian river
20 More uptight
21 Fisherman's gear
23 Raison d'—
25 Wallach of screen
26 — Alamos, NM
27 Corporate letters
30 Soft drinks
32 Ballerina's perch
34 Crumbled into dust
36 Frutti introduction
39 Sunburn soother
40 Traffic tie-up
43 Ollie's pal
44 Snooped, with "around"
46 Egyptian coins: var.
48 Historical time
49 Hearty brew
50 Pooh's pal
51 What's more
53 Busy, after "in"

55 Duffer's impediment
57 Diamond game
60 Soon, slangily
64 Uncomfortable, muscle-wise
65 Signed contract, e.g.
67 Pump
68 Cubicle
69 Ecuadorian dinero
70 Goes like a bunny
71 Air France hub
72 — time (never)

## Down

1 Dundee denizen
2 Popeye's prop
3 Neck-and-neck
4 Closely packed
5 "His Master's Voice" company, briefly
6 Toward sunrise
7 Fern's reproductive cells
8 Relating to pitch
9 Weevil's meal
10 Written address to one and all
11 Sal of screen
12 Defeats
14 Biting insect
18 Scoreboard column
22 Skater Katarina
24 Perfect place
27 David Bowie's wife
28 — contendere
29 Union-only workplace
31 Put a book on-screen, e.g.
33 Give the heave-ho to
35 "Doe a — . . ."
37 Poi base
38 — many words
41 Urban unrest
42 *Little Women* boy
45 Wattle and —
47 Greets the judge
49 Merchant
51 Make ashamed
52 Mexicali munchie
54 Vanzetti's partner
56 West of Venice
58 Hurricane centers
59 Take it easy
61 The Amish, e.g,
62 Yield, as interest
63 Jazz singer Laine
66 Like a fox

# Puzzle 1-42: Rhyme Time

The title gives you a key to how the theme entries work.

## Across

1 "It Must Be Him" crooner Vikki
5 Harvest goddess
10 Gambling game
14 ". . . — saw Elba" (end of palindrome)
15 Practical
16 Terrible Russian
17 Mirror image
19 The Crimson — (Alabama)
20 Alger Hiss accusation
21 Big-shouldered figure
22 Gear tooth
23 Paul Bunyan's tool
24 From A to Z
27 *The Magic Christian* band
33 Matinee —
34 Goofs
35 Dutch commune
36 Get on a horse
37 "Me, too"
38 *Picnic* playwright
39 Shirt shape
40 Bottled spirits
41 *Private Lives* author Coward
42 Whopper
44 16 Across, et al.
45 Light switch positions
46 Louis XIV, par exemple
47 "It ain't over till it's over" source
50 Guide dog
56 Guitarist Clapton
57 Neil Diamond film, with *The*
58 Andes capital
59 Go along with
60 Inner Hebrides island
61 More's partner
62 Nebs
63 Part of TA

## Down

1 Surrender
2 Olympian hawk
3 Gather wheat
4 Make fun of
5 Giving a signal
6 Sicilian spewer
7 Avenger Diana
8 Gen. Robert —
9 To be, Spanish style
10 Mitten loser
11 "— Ways" (Santana hit)
12 Zip, to Zapata
13 Change for a fin
18 Dentist's canal?
21 "—, Bold as Love" (Jimi Hendrix)
23 Big hairdos
24 Circumference
25 "Until tomorrow, mon amour"
26 It allows you to surf?
27 "— home the bacon"
28 Bandleader Shaw
29 Spoiler
30 Italian salami center
31 Lawn care device
32 Movie units
34 Lord Anthony and others
38 General's star, e.g.
40 Lollobrigida
43 Ladies' benevolent society
44 Singer Tenille
46 Greets the dawn
47 *For Whom the — Tolls*
48 Cat Nation member
49 Rolls around the hoop
50 Wise man
51 First name in poetry
52 Bk. before Daniel
53 Freudian subjects
54 Strong desires
55 Part of QED
57 Knockout punch setup

# Puzzle 1-43: Stacks of Seven

### Across

1 Encouraged
8 False fronts
15 Innocence
16 Check out
17 Halves
18 It's a peach
19 The loneliest number
20 *The Egg and I* family name
22 Hold back anger
23 Take it easy
25 Coral construction
26 Follower of Benedict
27 Marsh growth
29 Take chances
31 Big do
32 Rare meals
34 Carefully said
36 Determined
38 A tad
41 Tack room staple
45 Type of rock?
46 It may be on the house
48 Gave another viewing
49 Elec. unit

50 Titles in Toledo
52 Inane
53 Advanced math. course
55 Essential amino acid
57 Military address
58 Mighty Ducks milieu
60 Birthday suit
62 Where Mazatlan is
63 Recluse
64 Red-berried evergreen
65 Emulates Holmes

### Down

1 Opens a latch
2 Pirates' day off, perhaps
3 Ballet by Adam
4 When day is done
5 "All hands on —!"
6 Playful mammal
7 Made a home
8 "Be my guest"
9 Semi supporter
10 Semi puller
11 Cyclones' home
12 More sordid
13 International accord
14 Sushi wrapper
21 Ron Carey's group
24 Arco option
28 Bias
30 Chow
31 Paid for
33 Caustic comic Mort
35 Fly like an eagle
37 Sadie Hawkins Day sprinter
38 Mode for 33 Down
39 World of *1984*
40 Oscar winner Ray *(The Lost Weekend)*
42 Extreme
43 "The Pirate of the Gulf"
44 Menu selections
47 Hit squarely
51 Place for a paradiddle
54 Type of trout
55 Kimba or Simba
56 Gave the once-over
59 Chess rating system developer
61 Big bird

# Puzzle 1-44: Valentine's Day Trio

## Across

1 Uttered
5 Salvador, once
10 Homeric material
14 Villa-building family
15 Editorial abbr.
16 "O patria mia" singer
17 Sweet Valentine
20 The twos, they say
21 Approaches
22 Airline to Tel Aviv
23 Totes
25 Border crossing town
28 — Beach, FL
29 Movie monogram
32 "Easy — it!"
33 Secret police chief, once
34 *Mad About You* role
35 Fragrant Valentine
39 Building extension
40 Unconventional
41 Employs
42 Caustic substance
43 School grps.
44 Real —
46 Mix the salad
47 A Waugh
48 Recurrent theme
51 Handel's "Messiah"
55 Serious Valentine
58 Trim down
59 "Miss Muffet — a tuffet"
60 Author Bagnold (*The Chalk Garden*)
61 Skidded
62 Husband
63 H.S. hurdle

## Down

1 Order
2 1975 Wimbledon winner
3 "Take — leave it!"
4 Trim down
5 Site of the new Guggenheim
6 In any way
7 Loathe
8 Island in the Seine
9 Question
10 Comforts
11 Tower town
12 Baltic feeder
13 Backtalk

18 Artistic medium
19 Mr. Bergman
23 Ballerina's support
24 Settled
25 Ford heir
26 Humble
27 *The Old Wife's Tale* playwright
28 Anjou, etc.
29 Beethoven's — *Solemnis*
30 Welcome
31 Billiards play
33 Frat letters
36 Crown
37 Dumps
38 Consequences
44 May, famously
45 Bristle
46 Burned out
47 Passion
48 Charts
49 October birthstone
50 Garr of the movies
51 One of the Ringling Brothers
52 Columnist Barrett
53 "What's — for me?"
54 Bookie's concern
56 Ogee shape
57 Diagnostic scan

# Puzzle 1-45: Smorgasbord

## Across

1 Pakistani language
5 Kingsley or Martin
9 Protégé
14 Mideast canal
15 Italian port
16 Lyric poem
17 Two-time Women's Open winner
20 Collar style
21 "— Sera, Sera"
22 Discipline
26 Reduce
30 *Forty* —
31 Light carriage
32 Virginia coll.
33 — the beans (tell)
34 Letters that spell trouble?
35 Cadence
36 NHL Rookie of the Year: 1995
39 Feel sorry
40 Land of leprechauns
41 First name in bandleaders
43 Stage décor
44 Chalcedony
45 Collard —
46 Kind of bridge
48 Thanksgiving Day events
49 Weapon
50 Kind of fiber

51 17 and 36 Across, e.g.
59 In the lead
60 Player's pool
61 Korean river
62 Three-card —
63 Dam
64 Midterm follower

## Down

1 Dream Team team
2 Compete in a race
3 Study
4 Israeli weapon
5 Eases
6 Concrete worker
7 Common ore
8 Title for Paul McCartney
9 Indigence
10 Unexpected victory
11 Player's pool
12 Muckraker Tarbell
13 Sci-fi writer Stanislaw
18 "Polly, put the — on . . ."
19 =
22 Letters on a letter
23 Cheered up
24 Short aria: var.
25 Like the ocean
26 Task
27 Warded off
28 John Lennon album
29 Put a match to
31 Flynn prop
34 Fervid
35 Kentucky college
37 Domains
38 Cooper's product
39 Winter in L.A.
42 Snaky shape
44 Measure of progress
45 Collect
47 1978 Nobelist
48 Cupid-like figures
50 Tarzan's friend
51 Actor Waterston
52 "— is it?"
53 Poetic time of day
54 Command to Nellie
55 Core
56 Impost
57 High note
58 Total

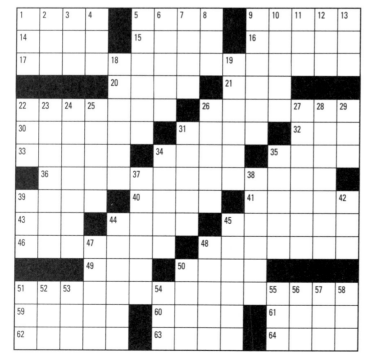

# Puzzle 1-46: Two Words in One

Entries draw from all sources, including the alphabet, as in 33 Down.

## Across

1 Ding follow-up
6 Course hazard
10 First name in country
14 Failure to react
15 Lock maker
16 Makes a boo-boo
17 Actress Verdugo
18 Public disorder
19 Barnyard sounds
20 Take care of picnic pests?
22 Peon
23 British rods
24 Anchors for runners
25 Slalom
28 Outside start
29 Adjective-forming suffix
31 Thwart
33 Platitudes
37 Conductor Klemperer
38 Andean
40 Finnish city
41 — Island dressing
43 Composition ender
45 Stormy blast
46 Type of artist?
47 Admit, with "in"
48 Constricted
51 Out of —
53 Well-known author
54 Crazy dance?
59 Lima's place
60 Inland Russian sea
61 Not a soul
62 At one time, at one time
63 Eric of Monty Python
64 Type of kitchen
65 Holy women, for short
66 Go-getter
67 Speak one's mind

## Down

1 Zone
2 Air
3 "— a kick . . ."
4 Before the ides
5 Recipient
6 Impossible boss
7 Claude of *Casablanca*
8 Scads
9 Strokes
10 Obstreperous king of the jungle?
11 DOS command
12 Circle Bar W, e.g.
13 Fools
21 Condemnation
24 Our uncle
25 Took a picture
26 Kin partner
27 Division word
29 Author Levin
30 Follow the rules
32 Money-mad types?
33 Trio after A
34 Like some personalities
35 Vogue competitor
36 Tallow base
39 Vane reading
42 Posed
44 Chants
46 More up-to-date
48 VCR needs
49 Sluggish
50 Furze
51 Dieter's bane
52 Summer ermine
54 Set, as the table
55 Mass calendar
56 Small bit
57 "Don't bet —"
58 Tropical state bird

# Puzzle 1-47: Knickknacks

## Across

1 Yonder
5 Naysayer
9 Flushing field
13 Buddhist monk
14 State bird of Minnesota
15 Garment lines
16 Knickknack
18 After-bath powders
19 Doddering
20 *Star Trek* crew member
22 Payment
23 Police informer: var.
25 Knickknack
27 "Wozzeck" composer
30 Tull's Anderson
32 Sutherland solo
33 Good serve
34 Catch of the day, sometimes
36 Cardiff's land
39 Knickknack
42 Sore one
43 Add up
44 Piece of mine
45 Emblem
47 Ruby or Sandra
48 Freshly
49 Knickknack

51 Buy on impulse, with "up"
53 Joplin composition
54 Cogwheel
57 Provision
61 Void
63 Knickknack
65 Versification
66 *The Twilight* —
67 Catch wind of
68 Rectangle part
69 Scratched out
70 Italian noble family

## Down

1 Father's robes
2 Cost of a ride
3 Notorious Ugandan leader
4 Indy activity
5 Guard of the Nibelung treasure
6 Scand. country
7 *Wind in the Willows* character
8 Quechua
9 Red or Dead
10 Milk container
11 Barker, e.g.
12 Balance sheet plus
15 Level connector
17 South of Tenn.
21 Airline monogram
24 Jeweler's weight
26 One-time phone feature
27 Wail
28 Lover of Narcissus
29 Arranged in a different order
31 Wanderer
34 Unkempt
35 Hills and —
37 Yeats' country
38 Slumgullion, e.g.
40 Arcade patron
41 Like a tight bite
46 Sodium hydroxide
48 Geronimo, e.g.
49 Links' hazards
50 Capital on the Red River
52 Fatima's husband
55 Woodworking tool
56 Player for Kasparov
58 Hawaiian instruments
59 Chair
60 Australian peninsula
62 Employ
64 Hydrogen's number

# Puzzle 1-48: Popular Pairs

When it comes to crossword repeaters, no sport is more popular in the missing-word category than 7 Down, which is a form of pelota or handball.

## Across

1 Waste maker
6 Pushovers
10 Sword's part
14 Started the pot
15 Nobelist Wiesel
16 Suffix in zoology
17 Impolite look
18 Pathway
19 Taunt
20 Popular pair
22 *Gentleman's Agreement* actress Celeste
23 Roth — (investment choice)
24 Puts down
26 Bring about
30 Martin's *Laugh-In* partner
32 Tide type
33 Street urchin
35 A dream come true, for example
39 Gem weight
41 "— Hear a Waltz?"
42 Andean pack animal
43 Gladiator's setting
44 "— girl!"
46 Pizzeria fixture
47 Parts of an ounce
49 On the cheap side
51 Times to the plate
54 Showery mo.
55 Thrash
56 Popular pair
63 Producer de Laurentis
64 *Born Free* subject
65 Promotional gimmick
66 Ides of March rebuke
67 *Cheers* actor Roger
68 Central Florida city
69 Take a load off
70 On the — (on target)
71 Aired again

11 Seville so-long
12 Old wives' tale
13 Swarms
21 Ms. Barrymore
25 Bondsman's money
26 Andean of old
27 At hand
28 "Bet you can't," e.g.
29 Popular pair
30 Public uprisings
31 "Think nothing —!"
34 *Bonanza* brother
36 Roof projection
37 Revival cry
38 Reel in, as a fish
40 Like a lemon pie
45 Sacred river in "Kubla Khan"
48 To the rear, in sailor-speak
50 Silver-tongued one
51 Puff — (venomous snake)
52 Hackneyed
53 Lays one down, on the ballfield
54 Make — for (defend)
57 Bread spread
58 Applications
59 "No more Mr. — Guy!"
60 Letter starter
61 Type of lizard, with "monster"
62 — equal footing

## Down

1 Corned beef —
2 Opposed to
3 Baseball card datum
4 Prefix meaning "trillion"
5 Like paradise
6 Alabama march site
7 Jai —
8 Specifies, with "down"
9 Playground fixture
10 Popular pair

# Puzzle 1-49: Paging Mrs. Malaprop

To crack this theme, think like Mrs. Malaprop, the matron from Sheridan's classic play *The Rivals,* who misuses words.

### Across

1 Saracen
5 Philippine island
10 Islets
14 Where there's a — . . .
15 Shut
16 Frenzied
17 "Say — drugs"
18 Attain
19 Depend (on)
20 Guest lecturer's stopover?
23 Impresario Hurok
24 Italian wine center
25 Coach Parseghian
28 Shade giver
30 Poetic word
31 "Not — bet!"
34 Type of orange
36 Feedbag filler
38 Parched
39 Viper's vegan vittles?
42 Broadway musical
43 Physics beginning
44 Leading
45 Still
46 Decide
47 Miss Clavel, of *Madeline*
49 Tolkien creature
50 Equipment
52 Glutton
54 Rooster's strut?
60 Gossip
61 Swank up
62 Part of R&R
64 Ruin
65 Dog-— (well-thumbed)
66 Give an impression
67 "I've — had!"
68 Pores over
69 *I Dream of Jeannie* actress Barbara

### Down

1 Wheat beard
2 Public disturbance
3 " — Rhapsody" (Brahms)
4 Explodes, with "up"
5 Go through a screen
6 A, in Tel Aviv
7 Castle feature
8 Author Sholem
9 Practice
10 Gem weight
11 Better
12 Egg element
13 It's often the limit
21 Coward and others
22 Literary monogram
25 Burned up
26 Street show
27 Modernist
29 French impressionist Claude
30 Hawke of film
32 Canon rival
33 Skilled
35 *TV Guide* notation
37 Part of DA
38 Sothern or Sheridan
40 Unseemly
41 Kind of boom
46 Former acorn
48 Bowls over
51 "Candle in the Wind" singer Sir —
53 Furze
54 Medoc, for one
55 Scot's "from"
56 Prefix meaning trillion
57 Pay attention to
58 Like some dorms
59 Swiss abstractionist Paul
60 Name
63 Trio after K

# Puzzle 1-50: Same Starters

Keep in mind that "starters" is crossword code for "prefixes."

## Across

1 Louis Pasteur on film
5 Crow
9 Rhyme scheme
13 Cape south of Flattery
15 Trick
16 Ballot
17 Hidden
19 Competent
20 They're often on the horn
21 Seasonal figure
23 Devour, with "up"
24 Furrow
25 Far apart
27 Piled up
29 Long and lean
30 Skater Midori
31 Corporate benefit
32 Strong point
33 Unsacred
34 On vacation
38 Author George
41 Sheds
42 A 49-day liturgical season
46 Hairdresser's stuff
47 "— and Soul"
48 Car trim
50 Brunch offerings
52 Pelt
53 Shooter or pack
54 Court ace Chris
55 Takes into custody
57 Catherine's husband
58 In a snit
61 Biblical word
62 Oil cartel
63 Wet land tract
64 Sugar source
65 Auto necessity
66 Multitude

## Down

1 Red head, once?
2 Wail
3 Spitz or Biondi, technically
4 Old-time actor Novello
5 Ekland from Sweden
6 Oriental exports
7 Furniture material
8 Becomes immersed
9 —-garde
10 Horse feature
11 1996 Olympic venue
12 Spelling —
14 Lit
18 Brother of King Faisal
22 Off-center
23 Sense of things to come?
25 Flits about
26 Beanie Baby, e.g.
28 MGM rival
29 High
32 Closes down
35 Earthy tone
36 Jolson song starter
37 Easter opener
38 Gone by
39 Land property
40 Raise
43 Mediterranean wind
44 Formal letter
45 Sergeant Preston's horse
48 Breaking waves
49 Ringlet
51 Dormouse
52 Monk's habit
55 "— o'clock scholar . . ."
56 Hog ladies
57 Bucket
59 "— creek"
60 Use a needle

# Puzzle 1-51: Members Only

**HINT**

Think NBC's *Today Show* when solving 1 Across.

*Across*

  1 Katie's cohost
  5 Accounting entry
 10 Scrub
 14 Wings for Pegasus
 15 Re-format
 16 Crafty maneuver
 17 Rational
 18 Charges
 19 Circle segments
 20 Grace Kelly film
 23 Kit —
 24 Late in the day, poetically
 25 Candidates
 27 Unser's wheels
 32 Long-ball pro golfer John
 33 Sculler's tool
 34 Pitchfork feature
 35 Flip side of verso
 38 God of thunder
 40 This screen has blips
 43 Alt.
 44 Clear jelly
 46 Early sch.
 48 Shoshonean
 49 Prepare apples
 51 Keep in mind
 53 Magazine types

 56 "— clear day . . ."
 57 Balloonist's need
 58 Saving plan
 64 Part of MIT
 66 Positive pole
 67 About
 68 Aptly named citrus fruit
 69 Lies
 70 Scored on a serve
 71 Sonnet, e.g.
 72 Bomb tryout
 73 Singing Mama

*Down*

  1 Fermented mixture
  2 Jai —
  3 Space drink
  4 Sneaky laugh
  5 Suave
  6 Julia's brother
  7 Pacific paradise
  8 Man and others
  9 Sampled
 10 Madrid Mrs.
 11 Deli order
 12 Pianist Levant
 13 They're a bother
 21 Faction
 22 Twelve months
 26 "Twittering Machine" artist
 27 Slate
 28 Sounds of delight
 29 Farmer's design
 30 Genetic letters
 31 Spring feast
 36 Head, in France
 37 Above and beyond
 39 Rumpus
 41 British beverage
 42 Least accessible
 45 Capt. Hook's nemesis
 47 List
 50 Corrections
 52 Zealot
 53 Mom's admonition
 54 San —
 55 French assembly
 59 Pineapple producer
 60 Middle March
 61 South American
 62 Underground deposits
 63 Beatty and Buntline
 65 One of LBJ's beagles

# Puzzle 1-52: Double-O

Some people live on forever in the Crossword Hall of Fame, such as Mrs. Charlie Chaplin. (See 2 Down.)

## Across

1 The —, a.k.a. Springsteen
5 Title for Agatha Christie
9 Binding
14 Burt's ex
15 Saran —
16 *Falstaff*, for one
17 Geraint's loyal lady
18 Popular Irish singer
19 Nymph
20 Site of Napoleon's defeat
22 Decorates
23 Will Rogers, to some
24 Rn
26 Diamond weight
29 Author Puzo
30 *Leaving — Vegas*
33 Nimble
34 Cupid's wings
35 *Legends of the Fall* star Brad
36 *Barney Miller* actor
38 Anxiety producer
40 Rick Majerus' team
41 End of Caesar's statement
43 Seattle's Key
44 Nancy Drew's beau
45 Physicist Nikola
46 Manservant
47 — Domingo
48 Mousse
49 West Pointers
52 Clamor
57 Build up
58 Ready, willing, and —
59 Ox kin
60 Slow, to Chopin
61 Sight out West
62 Guitarist Clapton
63 Riata
64 Seniors' party
65 Track meet event

## Down

1 Lost out, with "it"
2 Mrs. Chaplin
3 Agitated state
4 New York City features
5 Lived, poetically
6 Tuscan river
7 City election
8 DC watchdog
9 Haitian sorcery
10 Child's protective cover
11 Dirty look
12 Where to find Teheran
13 June honorees
21 Baptism, et al.
22 Farewell, in Fontainebleau
25 *Lawrence of —*
26 Atchafalaya Basin resident
27 Playground shooter
28 Prepared potatoes
29 "Red Book" follower
30 Slander
31 Observe Yom Kippur
32 Ermine
35 Struck, as with fear
37 Bakery fixtures
39 Attention-getter in court
42 Wipe out
45 *The Rose —* (Tennessee Williams)
47 Religious groups
48 Trace
49 Type of phone
50 Length x width
51 Where to find iniquity
53 In addition
54 Wife of Zeus
55 Kimono closers
56 "That hurt!"
58 Rock concert gear

# Puzzle 1-53: Literally Speaking

Follow the title of this puzzle closely when solving the theme entries!

## Across

1 Soft drinks
6 Cut short
11 "What — that all about?"
14 Scrap, as a takeoff
15 Destiny
16 Maven
17 Be careful?
19 Ft. Worth campus
20 Meander
21 Legal add-ons
23 Droopy-eared dog
26 Soft toppers
27 Took care of
28 Boneless serving
29 Flemish wall hanging
30 Oscar winner of 1955
31 Scammed
34 Sharp
35 Greeting, for Dolly
36 Short example
37 Hems and haws
38 Growing places
39 Spanish seaport
40 Rabbi's shawl
42 Easter event
43 Barn storage place
45 Old-time delivery folk
46 God of the winds
47 Units of sweat
48 Capote on B'way
49 Work week endings?
54 Geom. figure
55 Like a whistle
56 *Swan Lake* role
57 Giggling sound
58 Otherworldly
59 Hawaiian birds

## Down

1 Presidential nickname
2 Selling price equivocation
3 Ladies' room, in London
4 Clinton, originally
5 Thwarts
6 Pate base
7 Fit
8 Before, of yore
9 Almond liqueur
10 On the double
11 Bygones?
12 Capital of Ghana
13 Kids' Dr.
18 First name in reapers
22 Kangaroo's mom
23 Plumber's tool
24 More chaste
25 Policeman's pronouncement?
26 Rolls up
28 Soothes
30 Worth
32 Inorganic compound
33 Egg unit
35 Type of shoe repair
36 One aspect of The Force
38 Sashay
39 Where witches brew: var.
41 "That's — she wrote"
42 Chanteuse Edith
43 Devise, as a plot
44 Raptor retreat
45 Intervening
47 — B'rith
50 Done, to Donne
51 Commotion
52 It's on tap
53 Word of acceptance

# Puzzle 1-54: Lunar Sightings

The hose referred to in 21 Down is not the garden variety!

## Across

1 Blokes
6 Table setting
9 Wings for Pegasus
13 Copy, as in an antique shop
14 Part of NYU
16 Lucy's co-star
17 Fiery crime
18 Moore of *GI Jane*
19 Go-getter
20 Lunar fees?
23 Stab
24 Bruce or Laura
25 Gourd
28 Computer expression
31 Consumer activist Ralph
34 When some lunch hours begin
35 Uses a finger
37 What today's tires lack
39 Lunar resident?
42 "— the gate of the temple" (Gibran)
43 **Downy** duck
44 Pinocchio's downfall
45 Paris plaza
47 Undercover gov't grp.
48 Rank and —
49 Kansas town
51 Angle or cycle starter
53 Lunar serenade?
61 Opera highlight
62 Forbidding
63 Furious
64 Advance on credit
65 Seagull
66 "Maria —" (1933 song)
67 Sommer of screen
68 Become wise, perhaps
69 Cadence

## Down

1 Pull an "all-nighter"
2 Deli specialty
3 Lhasa — (dog breed)
4 ASAP
5 Navigational device
6 Roger of the news
7 Deauville donkeys
8 Shy
9 Supplement
10 Panetta of the White House
11 "Wait —" (one minute)
12 Land of leprechauns

15 Harpy
21 Hose material
22 One who blabs
25 Butter portions
26 System of principles
27 Michelangelo masterpiece
29 *Grapes of Wrath* extra
30 Leader of the Russian Revolution
32 Carlo Levi's *Christ Stopped at —*
33 Fix the squeak again
35 Guard
36 Codes of conduct: abbr.
38 Cut, old-style
40 Pickle, as fish
41 Warms over
46 Skip over
48 It's often grand
50 Greek market
52 Composer Ned
53 Maldive capital
54 Baseball's Hershiser
55 Sty cry
56 Posted a poster
57 Corner
58 Help
59 Fork feature
60 Month after Shevat

# Puzzle 1-55: Girl Power

### Across

1 Wine cellars
6 Type of roast
10 Take — view of (disapprove)
14 Ain't, the right way
15 Fit to serve
16 Jumped to one's feet
17 All-girl version of 1975 John Wayne flick?
19 Swig of white lightnin'
20 Merchant of song
21 Candy — (hospital aide)
23 Theatrical light material
24 Hold back
25 Dutch master Jan
28 Two cents, so to speak
29 Price word
30 Cuts down
31 Impact sound
32 Seuss turtle
35 High dudgeon
36 He dethroned Primo Carnera
38 It has a + or a -
39 Views
41 —-Locka, FL
42 Numero uno
43 Fog, Scottish style
44 Colony critter
45 Zest

46 Kind of mole
49 — Lanka
50 Tell, et al.
51 Eye doctor
55 Playboy
56 Member of all-girl square dance band?
58 Capri, e.g.
59 Saroyan character
60 *Beau* —
61 Writer Silverstein
62 Eyelid swelling
63 Use a VCR

### Down

1 "High Hopes" lyricist
2 Word with code
3 Let off steam
4 Confines, as an animal
5 — *Kisses* (Francois Truffaut film)
6 Rehnquist's uniform
7 Palindromic PM
8 Liverpool's river
9 Smarty-— (wise guy)
10 Ump, often
11 All-girl gatherings?
12 Duck's nesting place
13 British unit of length
18 Hodges of the diamond
22 Not so green
24 Vaudevillian
25 Hood's weapon
26 Garr of *Tootsie*
27 Run-down, all-girl style
28 Clinton's instrument
31 —-relief
32 Thumbs-up vote
33 Word on a reward poster
34 Inner prefix
36 Seine feeder
37 Well-put
40 North Carolina native
42 Abraham Levitt, for one
44 Put into pigeonholes
45 Feeling of ill will
46 Delhi dresses
47 Word with can
48 Predatory whales
49 HS subject
51 *All* — (1984 Steve Martin film)
52 Ingrid's role in *Casablanca*
53 Prepares the table
54 Unau's home
57 "— cool!"

# Puzzle 1-56: Anatomy Lesson

A given name in a clue indicates that the entry is also a given name as in 53 Down.

## Across

1 Swede's neighbor
5 Jazz improvisation
10 Gem from Australia
14 "— to leap tall buildings . . ."
15 Betel nut palm
16 Make the cut
17 Hotel for Elvis?
19 Anemia antidote
20 Fatima's husband
21 Hastens
22 Girders
24 Took another year
26 King David's composition
27 Faux —
28 Wool nibbler
29 Poetic palindrome
32 Savory jelly
35 Hit by The Kinks
36 Mine entrance
37 Three Stooges lunch order?
40 Where bobs may dangle
41 Declare
42 Shelves
43 Fabergé objet
44 Feels badly
45 "— Pete's sake!"
46 Habitat
48 Goes back on one's word
52 Ancient Greek region
54 *Riders of the Purple Sage* novelist
55 Zsa Zsa's sister
56 Uprising
57 Cause of mental exhaustion
60 Words on a memo
61 Slip of the tongue
62 Comic Johnson
63 — *of Heaven* (early Richard Gere film)
64 Early Ford
65 Winter Palace resident

## Down

1 Volcanic mudflow
2 White poplar
3 Unadorned
4 — cent
5 Coddles
6 Went wrong
7 Drones
8 Andes tuber
9 Neighbor of India
10 Bay window
11 EMT employee
12 Mighty mite
13 Refracting device
18 Hitting sound
23 Before "humbug"
25 Long stories
26 Word with opposite
28 Painter Grandma —
30 Moranis of *Honey, I Shrunk the Kids*
31 Number suffixes
32 African evergreen
33 Hawk's perch
34 Prelude to heaven
35 Water container?
36 With it
38 Praiseworthy
39 Spoke monotonously
44 Mythical beast
45 Italian herb
47 Chomps
48 Bring up
49 Transmission parts
50 Webber musical
51 More lucid
52 Like the Gobi
53 Mel's *Mad Max* co-star
54 Uses a laser
58 Unit of energy
59 Hamelin pest

# *Puzzle 1-57: Morse Play*

Gretna Green (2 Down) is a well-known place to tie the knot on impulse!

## *Across*

1 Pol. party
4 *The Bell Jar* author Sylvia
9 Poker Flat's chronicler
14 Ryan's *Love Story* co-star
15 River through Tours
16 Bermuda or Vidalia
17 Out-of-date printer
19 In a strange manner
20 Fiber-— cable
21 Holed, as a putt
23 Author LeShan
24 Troubadour's verse form
27 In apple-pie order
29 Utter disappointment
34 Field game
38 Rubberneck
39 Pueblo pot
40 Baker of song
43 Lamb's nom de plume
44 Observe Yom Kippur
46 Word processor's output
48 Signature spots
51 Blackthorn fruit
52 Got the picture
57 Gibson of *Lethal Weapon I, II, III,* and *IV*
60 Regan's father
62 Rocket stage

63 Legal excuse
65 Odometer locale
68 Well-oiled
69 A Barrymore
70 16.5 feet
71 Natural fence
72 Pop singer Taylor —
73 Crafty

## *Down*

1 Pedestal parts
2 Go to Gretna Green
3 Catcher's inventory
4 Tenor Domingo
5 Sodom refugee
6 Get out into the open
7 Speaker of Cooperstown
8 Colorless hydrocarbon
9 Oriental water pipes
10 Sonny-Cher link
11 Coney Island attraction
12 Let the cat out of the bag
13 Popular Irish singer
18 Campus in MA
22 Writer Buntline
25 Shuttle letters
26 Part of AMA
28 Tribal symbol
30 Spyri book
31 White as a sheet
32 Ireland, poetically
33 Usher
34 Laundromat unit
35 Kind of sax
36 Coagulate
37 Carries on
41 Grammy-winner Braxton
42 Served perfectly
45 Long and fishy
47 Fit for service
49 Anonymous John
50 Unlike today's gasoline
53 In the past
54 "— on my Pillow"
55 Sign up
56 — longlegs
57 Prepare spuds
58 *Vogue* rival
59 Fibbed
61 Pro — (proportionately)
64 Panhandle
66 Like a wallflower
67 Egg layer

# Puzzle 1-58: All Rise

## Across

1 Stop, at sea
6 Columbo, Spade, et al.
10 Partner of gloom
14 Scoundrel
15 Verve
16 Cooking pot
17 Not solid
18 Captain of fiction
19 — *Window* (Hitchcock classic)
20 Demand due observance of protocol
23 Obtain
24 Selvages
25 Cool — cucumber
28 Aries symbol
30 Shade of blonde
31 Posed
34 Missile container
36 Knock
38 Agave fiber
40 1933 Shirley Temple film
44 "Peter, Peter, pumpkin —"
45 "Fever" singer Peggy
46 Bristles
47 Three, in Torino
48 Dawn goddess
51 Hill builder
53 The Holy —
54 Clara or Rosa lead-in
56 Gel
58 Flag carriers
65 Nick and Nora's pooch
66 Smallish monster
67 Beauty parlor
68 Soft mineral
69 Blue pencil
70 Roman official
71 TV actor Estrada
72 CSA soldiers
73 Naturalist Edwin Way —

## Down

1 Sandy's comments
2 Fencing move
3 Water, south of the border
4 Litigious
5 Haymaker
6 Neighbor of AL
7 Vote in
8 Polaroid, e.g.
9 Night noises
10 Campus homes
11 Bread spread
12 Pearl Buck heroine

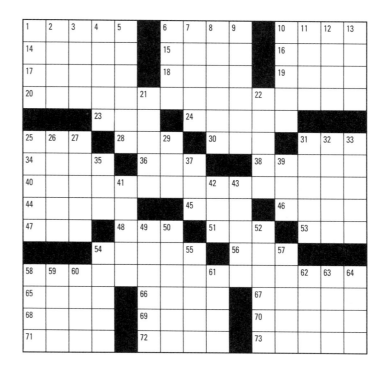

13 "Contrary" girl
21 Japanese seaport
22 Principle
25 Measure of wealth
26 Shankar's instrument
27 Like Pegasus
29 Plot out
31 Seethes
32 Coeur d'—
33 To the point
35 Singular
37 Chum
39 — Na Na
41 Fear
42 Cultural events funder: abbr.
43 Compact
49 Wild ass
50 Gait
52 Afternoon service
54 Munchie
55 Improvise
57 World — Center
58 Overfill
59 Ivan, e.g.
60 Mythical Hun
61 Belfry residents
62 Director Kazan
63 Bialy, for one
64 Snick's partner

# Puzzle 1-59: Yo Ho Ho and a Bottle of Rum

The title of a puzzle clues you in to the theme.

### Across

1 Archaeologist's find
6 Fundamental
11 "Mazel —!"
14 Central New York city
15 Banishment
16 Flagon filler
17 Ocean floor, to a pirate
20 TV Tarzan Ron
21 Kimono closers
22 Fragrant neckwear
23 Walk through muck
24 Hot sauce
27 Start of a sea song
31 Succulent plants
32 Pretentious
33 Lassie, for one
36 "The jig —!"
37 Issues a threat
39 Green tropical fruit
40 Campaigned for office
41 Timbuktu's country
42 Puts a penny to a penny
43 More of 27 Across
47 Like sandals
49 Acquire through effort
50 4,840 sq. yards
51 Gagarin or Andropov

52 Top of the sundial
55 Pirate's exclamation
60 Bo Derek film of 1979
61 Hotel digs
62 Discussion group
63 A little work?
64 Flight element
65 Color variation

### Down

1 Fresh
2 List ender
3 Ancient Roman historian
4 Unfriendly
5 Coaxes
6 Harmless
7 Issues a pink slip
8 Member of the fam.
9 Under the weather
10 Wall St. bigwig
11 Plunges, pirate style
12 — acid (soap ingredient)
13 Not recto
18 Wind instrument
19 Reunion attendees
23 See 64 Across
24 Sea bird
25 Picnic pests
26 Exclamation, after "oh"
27 *Vanity* —
28 Role for Ingrid
29 Going down, as a pirate ship
30 *West Side Story* heroine
34 Uses Visa
35 Essence
37 Balls of bills
38 Charitable contribution
39 Author E.J.
41 Fannie —
42 Puts a penny to a penny
44 Rocky letters
45 Spay
46 Delhi dress
47 Personal preference
48 Earth tone
51 The Abominable Snowman
52 Woman warrior of TV
53 Angry
54 Man, for one
56 Difficult letter for a lisper
57 In a — (stuck)
58 Actress Farrow
59 Humbug preceder

# Puzzle 1-60: Temperature's Rising

## Across

1 Manages
6 Chill
10 Speech problem
14 Veranda
15 Mrs. Copperfield
16 Sicilian resort
17 *Tosca,* for one
18 Jacket feature
19 Winged
20 1992 Olympic gold medalist
23 Brief reply?
25 Soap unit
26 "— Bailey" (comic strip)
27 Kitchen pot
31 Eagle's nest
32 Scored perfectly
33 JFK flier
36 Narrow valley
37 — Peak
39 Cracker spread
40 Snaky curve
41 Asian river
42 Ship from the Mideast
43 Capitol Hill affliction
46 Comply
49 WW II force
50 Pub order
51 Environmental phenomenon
55 Out on a —
56 Type of bean
57 Round rolls
60 Daredevil Knievel
61 Mideastern port
62 Bert's companion on "Sesame Street"
63 Head, in Le Havre
64 Spoofed, with "up"
65 Carried on

## Down

1 Naval noncom
2 Alley —
3 Headaches
4 Pale color
5 Walk lazily
6 Never or often
7 Fast horse
8 Big pots
9 Food
10 Guide
11 Small bay
12 Traffic jam
13 Analyze a sentence

21 Cary's *She Done Him Wrong* co-star
22 Require
23 Old saw
24 Seasonal songs
28 Container
29 Caulking material
30 Complete the cake
33 Restoring
34 Bessemer product
35 — Haute
37 Kneecaps
38 UN agency
39 "Four and twenty blackbirds baked in a —"
41 *Star Wars* character
42 Policeman
43 Small stone
44 Type of fool
45 English river
46 Shoelace tip
47 Author Cussler
48 Halley's —
52 Last word of a dentist's request
53 Final word
54 Screenwriter Ephron
58 Let sleeping dogs —
59 Argumentative word, in old Rome

# Puzzle 1-61: Run of the Mill

Roman numerals are popular crossword entries, as in 48 Across.

**Down**

1 Witty
2 Tips off
3 Hooligan
4 Monkeyshine
5 "Henry Aldrich" star Stone
6 Man on the move
7 Singer Williams
8 Tyrant
9 Have no use for
10 Journey
11 Arthur Murray setting
12 Precede in time
13 Gridiron stats
21 Hose
22 Poetic palindrome
26 Yemeni port
29 Bar code and number combo
30 0
31 Battery part
32 French artist Bonheur
33 Joe Black portrayer Brad
34 Mel or Jose
35 Hyde Park buggy
36 Terrestrial crustacean
37 Watch with a dial: var.
38 Common cowboy name
39 Showtime competitor
43 To's companion
44 Queen's hometown
45 Catalan dish
46 Name of six popes
47 Stuck one's toe in
49 Feminist Eleanor
51 Passport stamps
53 Add spice to the wine
54 Feel for
55 Back to square one
56 Pause
57 Amazon tributary

50 Steer clear of
52 Freight hauling trucks
57 Lock horns
58 Dinesen or Borge
59 Maxi feature
60 Singer Abdul
61 Mesabi exports
62 Wings, Roman style
63 — *for Adano*
64 Small salamander
65 Make smooth

## Across

1 Brewed coffee
5 Mild exclamation
9 Ready to strike
14 Pearl Buck character
15 Old TV show *The Twilight* —
16 Trademark
17 Lincoln is here
18 1990 World Series champs
19 Sword handles
20 Best Picture of 1980
23 Mike Hammer portrayer Keach
24 Hockey great Bobby
25 Letters on a can
27 Req. for potential citizens
28 Crescent-shaped
32 The Beatles' album *Abbey* —
33 Arrive unannounced
34 Historian Shelby
35 Undercover cops
40 Makes a fuss
41 *The Sheltering Sky* actress Winger
42 Med. school course
43 Biceps, for one
45 Butter portion
48 Mid sixteenth-century date
49 Full house, for short

# Puzzle 1-62: White House Residents

Another clue for 33 Across is "Actor Wallach."

### Across

1 Initial
6 Strip
10 Sword's handle
14 Bellowing
15 Saint Columba's island
16 Euclid's lake
17 President 1850-1853
20 Wheelhouse dir.
21 Electrical charge
22 Fortune
23 Hetty Sorrel's love
24 Aries symbol
25 "Possession" poet
26 Light amplifier
29 Quotes
31 Taken aback
33 Inventor Whitney
34 "Nessun dorma" from *Turandot*
38 President 1885-1889
41 Fill to the gills
42 Start of the Musketeer credo
43 In total
44 Keillor's medium
46 Mutes, with "down"
47 Belief system
50 Summer sign
51 — in the neck
53 President 1981-1989
55 Steinbeck title direction
56 Cobbler's tool
59 President 1897-1901
62 Involved with
63 Marcel Marceau, for one
64 Type of down
65 Type of tide
66 Mild expletive
67 Garden tool

18 Reel's partner
19 Margarita garnish
23 Eager —
24 Get one's goat
26 Falls behind
27 City on the Jumna
28 Golf stroke
29 Casals' instrument
30 Imperial Valley "Sea"
32 Brand recognition
35 April forecast
36 Concerning
37 Picnic coolers
39 Muse of history
40 Beings
45 Jai —
47 Author Shaw
48 View from the Left Bank
49 Former British colony
51 Went to and fro
52 Get on bended knee
54 Slime
55 Gwyneth Paltrow film
56 Hawkeye portrayer
57 Garden intruder
58 Erato's instrument
60 Russian fighter plane
61 Tuck's partner

### Down

1 Fortune's partner
2 Rainbow goddess
3 Function
4 Mineo of screen
5 Cross
6 Walk like a crab
7 SoHo space
8 *Wheel of Fortune* purchase
9 Chatty
10 Shortens a skirt
11 Starbuck's selling point
12 Shows the door
13 Canines

# Puzzle 1-63: Speaking of Star Trek

Wordplay rules where you see a question mark at the end of a clue.

The crossword grid (filled in by hand):

| | | | | | | | | | | | | | |
|S|L|A|M| |E|D|A|M| |D|E|N|E|S|
|N|A|V|Y| |X|E|N|A| |I|R|I|S|H|
|O|T|I|S| |H|E|E|L| |S|I|G|M|A|
|W|H|A|T|S|U|P|W|I|T|H|C|H|E|W| |
|Y|E|N| |O|M|B| |O|U|S|T| |
| |D|I|E| |C|A|R|P| |C|Y|D|
|A|D|E|A|L| |O|I|L|S| |A|L|O|U|
|S|I|G|N|S|O|F|G|O|O|D|L|U|K|E|
|H|O|Y|A| |P|L|A|T| |R|O|B|O|T|
|E|S|P| |G|E|A|R| |J|O|E| |
| |T|H|O|R| |P|E|W| |A|T|A|
|L|E|I|A|W|A|K|E|A|T|N|I|G|H|T|
|A|W|A|R|E| |E|L|I|S| |V|E|I|L|
|R|E|N|T|S| |N|I|N|A| |E|N|A|
|A|S|S|E|T| |T|E|E|M| |S|A|G|S|

## Across

1 Sharif success
5 Dutch cheese ✓
9 Valleys ✓
14 "In the —" (Village People hit of 1979) ✓
15 Warrior princess of TV ✓
16 Notre Dame's Fighting — ✓
17 Elevator maker ✓
18 Bounder
19 Frat letter ✓
20 Greeting to a Wookiee?
23 Hankering
24 Mantra chants
25 Unseat
26 — *Hard* (Bruce Willis thriller) ✓
27 Nag
29 Dancer Charisse ✓
32 TV show *Let's Make* — ✓
35 Manet's medium
36 Moises or Felipe of baseball
37 Four-leaf clovers to Skywalker?
40 Patrick Ewing, once ✓
41 — du jour (menu special)
42 R2D2, for one
43 Kreskin specialty ✓
44 Equipment
45 Singer Jackson
46 Norse god of thunder

## Down

1 *The Man From — River* ✓
2 Shop class machine
3 Like Tweety
4 Interactive PC game
5 Unearth ✓
6 Briny bottoms
7 Once more
8 African nation ✓
9 Serve the stew
10 Clapton and namesakes ✓
11 Rick's American Café, for one
12 Salinger heroine
13 *Pygmalion* playwright ✓
21 Tarnishes ✓
22 Trunk
26 Funnyman Carvey ✓
27 Groucho Marx prop ✓
28 "Thanks —!"
30 John's wife ✓
31 Simon and Garfunkel, e.g.
32 Former Davis Cup captain ✓
33 "Vaya con —" ✓
34 King Tut, et al. ✓
35 *The Man — Mancha* ✓
36 Medicinal plant ✓
38 *Falstaff* or *Norma*
39 Hide, as sorrows ✓
44 Horace Greeley's advice
45 Relief for a sinking ship?
47 *The Luck of Roaring Camp* author
48 *Common Sense* writer ✓
49 Booster rocket ✓
50 Addams Family creature ✓
51 Broad-shouldered symbol
52 Zhivago's love ✓
53 Flock members
54 Superman's alter ego ✓
55 Novelist Wiesel ✓
56 Folksinger Burl ✓

48 Sunday seat ✓
49 One day — time ✓
52 What a princess with insomnia may do?
57 Cognizant
58 Yale men
59 Disguise
60 Leases ✓
61 One of Columbus' trio
62 Sicilian resort
63 Balance sheet plus ✓
64 Swarm
65 Droops

# Puzzle 1-64: Watch Your Step

## Across

1 Ringo
6 Wheel projection
9 Severity
14 Hanna-Barbera doggie
15 "Born in the —"
16 Meaningless
17 Blue jay's giveaway
18 Corn crib
19 Mixed, as by melting
20 Verbal gaffes
23 "Nonsense!"
24 Teacher's —
25 Idiot follower?
29 Newspaper page
31 Can you dig it?
34 Skirt style
35 Pavarotti piece
36 Sun Dance dancers
37 PC user's disasters
40 Radio shock-jock Don
41 Straight up
42 Skein formers
43 Beantown, for short
44 Sax player Getz
45 Baseball's Daulton
46 Dinghy necessity
47 Apiece
48 David Livingstone discovery of 1855
55 Evita portrayer LuPone
56 "— Gratis Artis"
57 World Cup scores
59 Green-card applicant
60 Hood's handgun
61 Shoelace tip
62 Easily irked
63 "Have you — wool?"
64 Geared up

## Down

1 Bag, for Brigitte
2 Surf and — (menu selection)
3 Teen follower?
4 Respond to reveille
5 What aces aren't
6 Eighteen inches, give or take
7 Where the Amu Darya flows
8 *Magic Mountain* author
9 Searched, with "through"
10 Greenland native
11 Shocked response
12 Till compartment
13 Kind of alert

21 Internet address separator
22 Pickle serving
25 Sir, in colonial India
26 "Remember the —" (battle cry of 1836)
27 PC prankster's creation
28 Added stipulations
29 Kin of Mork
30 Early Scot
31 Wise beginning
32 Ebbets Field shortstop
33 Ruhr industrial hub
35 On the main
36 —-friendly
38 Emcee's remarks
39 Lab gelatin
44 Sleek
45 Three after C
46 Piece for eight
47 Pallid
48 Singer Jerry
49 "How sweet —!"
50 Sitar selection
51 Land on the Caspian
52 Shea Stadium section
53 "Ooh" follow-up
54 Iditarod vehicle
55 Mrs. Nixon
58 Boar's abode

# Puzzle 1-65: Name Game (Monogram)

## Across

1 Salon special
5 Vassar, after 1969
9 — layer
14 *La Traviata* tune
15 Gumbo ingredient
16 *Saturday Night* —
17 Host of "American Bandstand"
19 It keeps you cool
20 Whale unit
21 Paris campus
23 *Animal Farm* ringleader
25 It gets stubbed
26 *Desire Under the* —
30 Garth portrayer
36 Yannick of tennis
37 Type of trip
38 Coquette
39 Classic Frank Herbert novel
40 Capital on the Willamette
43 Court proceedings
44 Politician Kefauver
46 Coach Parseghian
47 Pool hall sticks
48 Formerly Mrs. Cary Grant
51 Pungent
52 Summer cooler
53 Evian or Vichy

55 Gave unsolicited advice
60 Elaborate
65 Highly skilled
66 Popular sitcom star
68 Get a new — on life
69 Michigan, for one
70 Member of Parliament
71 "Peter, Peter, pumpkin —"
72 Pitcher
73 Life of Riley, e.g.

## Down

1 Tablets
2 Guitarist Clapton
3 Like Croesus
4 Shark on the menu
5 Butts heads
6 Volga feeder
7 Blows it
8 Black Hills locale
9 Bucking the trend
10 *The Producers* actor Mostel
11 Pizza place
12 Vegas gas
13 Sea eagle
18 "NYPD Blue" type
22 Mythical bird
24 Smitten
26 Wrapped up
27 Inferior quality
28 — ray
29 Star of *Apocalypse Now*
31 Fireballer Ryan
32 Get angry, e.g.
33 Outer spaces?
34 Fragrant compound
35 Beer ingredient
41 Son of Aphrodite
42 Brute strength
45 Head for the hills
49 Woodworker's tool
50 ". . . a — in a haystack"
54 Eyebrow shape
55 Greens
56 Light bulb, to Popeye
57 Make tracks, with "it"
58 — *dixit*
59 Challenge at the OK Corral
61 Hair-raising place
62 Word with code
63 Tiger gear?
64 Fontaine role of 1944
67 Make do

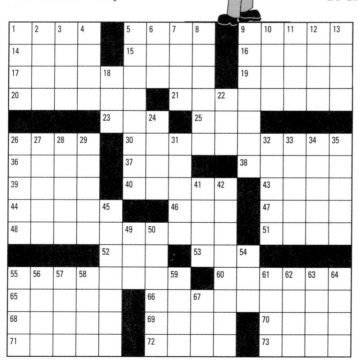

# Part II
## Sunday Puzzle Fun

The 5th Wave                    By Rich Tennant

"It's Deep Blue. After beating Garry Kasparov in chess, we tried feeding it The New York Times crossword puzzle, and after about an hour, the whole thing just crashed."

# *Puzzle 2-1: First Positions*

## Across

1 Assess, with "out"
6 Type of poodle
9 — *in America* (1985 Albert Brooks film)
13 Cattle movers
18 Deciduous shrub
19 Ms. Chanel
20 "Lonely Boy" singer
21 Ear-related
22 Begin the show
25 Abrade
26 The Princess Royal
27 *Madame* — (Simone Signoret film)
28 Like the desert
29 Bent forward
30 Dated, with "out"
32 Blair's predecessor
34 Scallopini
35 Wise up
38 Collar
39 Remove from the bottle
40 Bee follower
43 Strong snake
44 Begin the game
48 Rap sheet box
50 Hastens
51 Fast time
52 Astringent
53 Carry on
54 Press agent?
56 Merchandise mover
57 Khaniá's island
58 Begin to make progress
62 Cop's nemesis
63 Crust ingredient
64 Paddle
65 Haydn, familiarly
66 House on the Hill
69 Begin the card game
76 Skirt style
77 Red vegetable
78 Long times
79 Babe's brethren
80 Uprising
81 Gullible ones
82 Meadow
84 Stage whisper
85 Begin again
90 Mr. Iacocca
91 When the French fry
92 Off-color
93 Coffeepot

94 Showed off
96 Plaster backing
97 Hitches the team
99 Frigate's front
100 Consent under pressure
103 Essence
104 Radiant energy: prefix
106 Finishes the cake
110 Painting on a wall
111 Begin again
114 Writing
115 Declare
116 Yeats country
117 Pompeii sights
118 Hemmed
119 Hardy heroine
120 Freudian subject
121 *Breathing Lessons* byline

## Down

1 Poet Teasdale
2 Braveheart unit
3 Frigg's spouse
4 Money in Madrid
5 Poetic contraction
6 Does like a ballerina
7 William of —
8 "— are my sunshine . . ."
9 American architect Benjamin H.
10 *Today Show* sign
11 Pallet
12 Catch some rays
13 Miss America —
14 Unpopulated
15 Algerian port
16 Stun
17 Iditarod vehicle
19 Necklace
23 Fidelity
24 Indian rulers
29 Last but not —
31 Table scraps
33 Cost of cards
34 Author Jules
35 Type of power
36 Its motto is "Dirigo"
37 "No way" follow-up
39 Handle
40 *The Alienist* author Carr
41 Extract with solvent
42 Fudd of the funnies
43 Nasty remark

45 ". . . on a — and a prayer"
46 Spanish pudding
47 West Indies isle
49 Maiden hunter of myth
54 Letters on a memo
55 Football player Grange
56 Ride the Internet
57 Contend (with)
59 *Kiss Me, —*
60 Drubbing
61 Dunderhead
62 Cheers
65 Mom and pop org.
66 Bilko, e.g.
67 *Old Possum's Book of Practical Cats* author
68 Daughter of Tantalus
69 Indian soldier
70 Pianist Myra
71 Salivate (over)
72 Boardwalk birds
73 Send to Elba, e.g.
74 Gave up
75 Place for a banjo
77 Baker's dozen, perhaps

81 Compete with Baiul
82 Nepalese soldier
83 Bowling alley
84 Dynamic lead-in
86 Held protectively
87 Some Wall Streeters
88 Confront
89 Iranscam's Oliver
95 Conway of country
96 Tenant's document
97 "Help!"
98 Parsley unit
100 Elec. units
101 Remedy
102 Boast
103 Type of diamond setting
105 Meatball —
107 Industrialist Icahn
108 Diva Mills
109 Galactic bit
111 Auto finisher?
112 Cost of entry
113 Minded the baby

# Puzzle 2-2: Driver's Ed.

**HINT** Another clue for 76 Across is "Cleopatra's nemesis."

| 1 | 2 | 3 | 4 | | 5 | 6 | 7 | 8 | | 9 | 10 | 11 | 12 | | 13 | 14 | 15 | 16 |
|---|---|---|---|---|---|---|---|---|---|---|---|---|---|---|---|---|---|---|
| 17 | | | | | 18 | | | | | 19 | | | | | 20 | | | |
| 21 | | | | | 22 | | | | | 23 | | | | | 24 | | | |
| 25 | | | | 26 | | | | 27 | | | | 28 | | 29 | | | | |
| | | | 30 | | | | 31 | | | 32 | | 33 | | | | | | |
| 34 | 35 | 36 | | 37 | | 38 | 39 | | 40 | | | 41 | | 42 | | | 43 | 44 |
| 45 | | | | 46 | | | | 47 | | 48 | | | 49 | | 50 | | | |
| 51 | | | 52 | | 53 | | | | 54 | | 55 | | | 56 | | 57 | | |
| 58 | | | | 59 | | 60 | | | | 61 | | | 62 | | 63 | | | |
| | | | 64 | | 65 | | | | | | 66 | 67 | | | | | | |
| 68 | 69 | 70 | | | | | 71 | | | | | | 72 | | 73 | 74 | 75 |
| 76 | | | | 77 | | 78 | 79 | | 80 | | | 81 | | 82 | | | | |
| 83 | | | 84 | | 85 | | | 86 | | 87 | | | 88 | | 89 | | | |
| 90 | | | | 91 | | 92 | | | 93 | | 94 | | | | 95 | | | |
| | | 96 | | | 97 | | 98 | | | 99 | | | 100 | | 101 | | | |
| 102 | 103 | | | | 104 | | 105 | | | 106 | 107 | | | | 108 | 109 | 110 | |
| 111 | | | | 112 | | 113 | | | 114 | | | | | 115 | | | | |
| 116 | | | | 117 | | | | | 118 | | | | | 119 | | | | |
| 120 | | | | 121 | | | | | 122 | | | | | 123 | | | | |

## Across

1 Angelica of *Rugrats*
5 "Como — usted?"
9 Merit badge holder
13 Word before "happy"
17 Mansard extension
18 Clinch, with "down"
19 "Do you come here often?" e.g.
20 Chaste
21 Divisible by two
22 German crowd?
23 Word-of-mouth communication
24 Off-kilter
25 TRUNK ITEM
28 The Baby Boom era, e.g.
30 Forever and a day
31 — *homo*
33 See the sights
34 The works

37 Long in the tooth
40 Truck stop sign
42 Give benediction (to)
45 Perjure oneself
46 *Faust* figure
48 Went through the —
50 From the top
51 Mr. Baldwin
53 Beam fastener
55 Cozy corner
57 *Dernier* —
58 Walk like Mick Jagger
60 Treasures
62 "God Save the Queen," e.g.
64 TRUNK ITEM
68 50:50 chance
71 Get the lead out?
72 Trigger-happy
76 Egyptian snake

77 Midterm
80 It goes with kicking
82 New York state flower
83 Before dunk
85 Ham's dad
87 Chicago expressway, after "The"
89 — Ysidro, CA
90 Mosque text
92 Type of plum
94 Lest
95 Crude shelter
96 Passion personified
98 First name in jazz
100 Intense anger
102 Part of AARP
105 TRUNK ITEM
111 Hibernia
112 Bonkers
114 Scottish isle
115 Composer Khachaturian
116 Pressing
117 Shampoo additive
118 "A — time ago . . ."
119 Small monkey
120 Palmist
121 —-do-well
122 Beginning of Massachusetts motto
123 A coast

## Down

1 Gripe
2 The Beatles' guru Shankar
3 Profess
4 Uptight
5 Jeopardize
6 Delhi dress
7 Neck-and-neck
8 Homologous
9 Miniature racer
10 Tune
11 Ginger—
12 Spartacus, e.g.
13 Kitchen utensil
14 TRUNK ITEM
15 Square footage
16 Nobleman
26 _The Wind in the Willows_ character
27 Diamonds, slangily

29 Kind of story
32 School of princes
34 "Woe!"
35 See 10 Down
36 Satyrical look
38 What Pandora released
39 Golfer's gouge
41 Jack of _Barney Miller_
43 "Arid"
44 Dog-paddle
47 Flood foiler
49 Little Lipizzaner
52 Northside nine
54 — cotta
56 Femur-tibia connection
59 Track type
61 Richter, for one
63 Anastasia's ancestor
65 Ready for business
66 Stage whisper
67 Cut at an angle
68 Mowing, e.g.
69 Sonja Henie's birthplace
70 TRUNK ITEM
73 "Jeepers!"
74 Isaac's eldest
75 Sign a lease
78 1975 Abba hit
79 Spun yarn?
81 Farm feed
84 Popeye, perhaps
86 Patrolman's wear
88 Medieval peasant
91 Hide-hair link
93 Part of REO
97 Minivan alternative
99 Spry
101 Thrill
102 Beatty movie
103 Mills of opera
104 Valley
106 When the bell rings
107 Raggedy and others
108 Soprano's specialty
109 "Phooey"
110 Send out
113 Challenger

# Puzzle 2-3: Familiar Words

## Across

1 Fell, with "down"
5 Evening wrap
10 "Tall ship" features
15 Ms. Barrymore
19 Sweet place
20 Engages
21 Nebraska city
22 Greek letter
23 Thunderstruck
24 Map collection
25 Fixed the candle
26 — Spumante
27 With love
29 Blessed —
31 Author Sigrid (*Kristin Lavransdatter*)
33 Any of HOMES
34 A cowlick, perhaps
35 Place to hang your hat
36 Way in

39 Cultural lead-in
40 Lees
44 Spill the beans
45 Eye color
46 Midterm follow-up
47 Teacher's org.
48 Paddles
49 Gives in
50 Garden variety bloom
51 French holy women: abbr.
52 Geller of spoon fame
53 Rails
54 Scow
55 Poets
56 Train signal
58 Slight coloring
59 Coast-to-coast flight
60 Ship's cargo area
61 Type of musical composition
62 *Sunday in the Park — George*

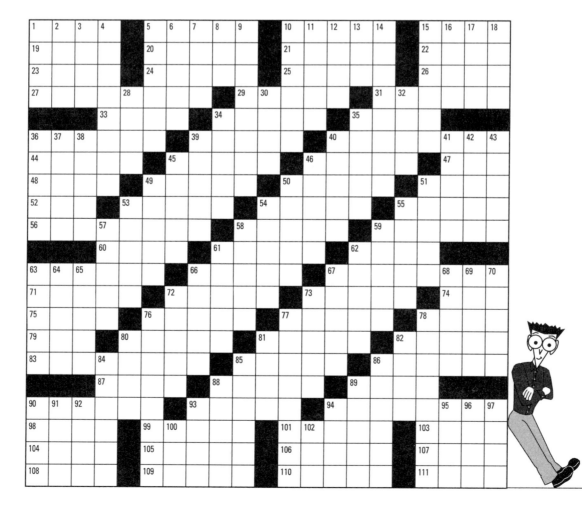

63 Menthol cigarettes
66 Brazilian bikini style
67 Halloween getups
71 Chaplin role
72 Plains home
73 Throttle
74 Pint-sized order
75 Ready to eat
76 Worked up
77 Unfriendly
78 French fromage
79 Cleo's nemesis
80 Flavorsome
81 Curlicue on a letter
82 Type of broom
83 Harangued
85 Falls flat
86 Boxes in a ring
87 Auto man Eli Ransom
88 Mr. Yeltsin
89 Sixties style
90 Behave as a codependent
93 Composer Harold ("Over the Rainbow")
94 Unfriendly manner
98 *The — Ranger*
99 Christened
101 Delicate layer
103 Swoosh originator
104 Carson's successor
105 French pupil
106 Filmmaker Sidney
107 Pennsylvania port
108 Controversial orchard spray
109 Early Kevin Bacon film
110 TV awards
111 Cleave

## Down

1 Shoot the breeze
2 Hockey bigwig Gordie
3 Warning
4 Sidewalk salesmen
5 Deep-sea killers
6 Lord or Lady
7 Paris hub
8 Meadow
9 Cores
10 Broadway star Rita
11 Change a contract
12 Season
13 Weatherman's letters
14 *— Night Fever*
15 Coronet
16 Supreme Diana
17 Kitchen ending
18 "Hold it!"

28 Sunrise direction
30 Bridal gear
32 Singer Diamond
34 Seeps
35 Wound up
36 *There's Something — Mary*
37 Cuban cigar
38 Objet
39 Nobel Prize winner of '78
40 Scorch
41 — *nous* (confidential)
42 Impoverished
43 Café cup
45 King of Judea
46 1996 Coen brothers film
49 Lowers the thermostat
50 Zoo attraction
51 Hindu holy man
53 Off-Broadway dance show
54 Indulge one's appetite
55 Legendary actress Davis
57 Motif
58 Photocopy fill
59 — *Business* (Tom Cruise film)
61 Corralled
62 *To the Lighthouse* author
63 Shoulder —
64 Get up
65 People of the North
66 Lukewarm
67 Funny Rock
68 Bog
69 Poet T.S.
70 Appears
72 Uses a keyboard
73 Where dogs congregate
76 Set, as cement
77 Florida native
78 Tyro
80 Broker's advice
81 Hurting
82 Tie up
84 Beginning of Hamlet's soliloquy
85 More aggressive
86 Prime cuts
88 Alla —: mus.
89 Moolah
90 Cinders of comics
91 Christmas standard
92 — *Karenina*
93 Last word
94 DC Dept.
95 Joyce's land
96 There's more than one way to — . . .
97 Tournament rank
100 The Great One
102 — *Beispiel* (for example)

# Puzzle 2-4: Double Features

## Across

1 Abound
5 — over fist
9 Unveil
13 *A — Rain's A-Gonna Fall*
17 Model Macpherson
18 Art Deco illustrator
19 Friendly introduction
20 Gallimaufry
21 William Powell/Cary Grant double feature?
25 Where rubber meets road
26 Ran, as dye
27 Wise start
28 "Encore!"
31 Double agent
33 Sections
34 Billy Bob Thornton/Harrison Ford double feature?
39 Suspended
40 New Haven university
41 Hoosegow
42 WWW address
45 "Are we there —?"
46 — la vie
47 Prom partner
49 Frank of The Mothers of Invention
51 Clumps
52 Architect Saarinen
53 More seductive
54 Jack Lemmon/Will Smith double feature?
59 Take turns
60 Burden
61 *Truth or* — (Madonna title)
62 Sermon okays
63 Seaweed
64 *— Breckenridge*
65 Frat party staple
68 *Close to the Edge* band
69 Thurman of *The Avengers*
70 Rank's partner
71 Skin
72 Robert DeNiro/Kevin Costner double feature?
77 Mrs. Bunker
79 Land of the leprechauns
80 Leases
81 Publicity —
82 Salinger heroine
84 *— Is Your Life*
86 George Burns/Spencer Tracy double feature?
93 Tardy
94 A — apple
95 Precedes "faith" and "ol' boy"
96 Ersatz butter
97 Yoko and family
98 Birthmarks
99 Stormy weather
100 Requirement

## Down

1 — Aviv
2 Student at 40 Across
3 Santa's helper
4 Business appointment
5 Scion
6 First name from *Laugh-In*
7 Advanced degree
8 — Leppard (rock group)
9 Scarlett's married name
10 Arthur of the court
11 Film critic Rex
12 Blow it
13 Owl
14 Maui greeting
15 *The Sun Also* —
16 Mover and shaker
22 Prayer partner
23 Ready, willing, and —
24 Clinton's second
28 Pale
29 Adhesive
30 *— Misbehavin'*
31 Type of vinegar
32 Keats poem
33 Cape outside Boston
35 Wave words
36 Riata
37 Author Sinclair
38 Maiden name lead-in
42 Capital of Western Samoa
43 Cartel since '60
44 Harmless prank
46 Ancient Egyptians
47 Object
48 Mars, in Greece
49 Urban street crossing
50 Spindle
51 Narc
52 Author Ferber
53 Caught
54 *The Picture of Dorian* —
55 The Eternal City
56 Shoshone Indians
57 Boston hub
58 Romantic poem

**63** "What kind of fool — . . ."
**64** Roger Bannister's race
**65** *Young Frankenstein* star Madeline
**66** *Quod* follower
**67** Tiara material
**69** Word of revulsion
**70** Flying object?
**71** Organist Billy
**72** Does the dishes
**73** Aleutian outpost
**74** Sign of spring
**75** "Muy —, gracias"
**76** *Exodus* author

**77** Green Mountain Boy Allen
**78** Because of
**81** Historic Normandy town
**82** To be: Lat.
**83** Switchblade
**84** Dupe
**85** Jekyll's alter ego
**87** Bert Bobbsey's twin
**88** Fabergé collectibles
**89** Anaconda kin
**90** Cheer for Manolete
**91** Like Willie Winkie
**92** *East of Eden*

# Puzzle 2-5: Get Going

Sometimes one clue suffices for all theme entries.

## Across

1 George Michael group of yore
5 Traffic sign
9 Urgent letters
13 Whitewash
17 *Mama's Family* character
18 Kiss follower
19 Director Jordan (*The Crying Game*)
20 Matinee —
21 Fido's friend
22 Outlet of the Cuyahoga
23 Miami's county
24 In the dumps
25 Get going
28 *Pigeon* — (John Updike collection)
30 Cameo, e.g.
31 *The Forsyte* — (John Galsworthy)
33 Howard Carter's discovery
34 Computer key
37 Notice
39 Gainesville student
43 Keats volume
44 Future flounder
46 Red qualifier
48 Singer Thomas
49 Have a hunch
51 Tommie of the Mets
54 Classic car
55 Look before you —
56 Become, with "up"
57 Porch
60 Long-suffering
62 Lettuce arrangement
63 Reasoning
65 Prepared
66 Withstands
70 Like a bread knife
72 Ship's pronoun
75 Rude dude
76 Atlas page
78 Crack the books
79 Back tooth
81 Heifer's home
82 Glow
84 — *and Sympathy*
86 Party pooper
87 Divvy up
89 Tenant
92 Cleopatra's —

94 Psychic Geller
96 Coast Guard woman
97 Icy coating
98 Rake over the coals
102 Get going
107 Jezebel's husband
108 Dryer residue
110 Casement
111 Word with muscle
112 Opposite of all
113 Sacramento arena
114 Ultimatum word
115 Hot spot
116 Best-selling author Wayne
117 Rendezvous
118 Hunter's quarry
119 Woodwind

## Down

1 "When you — upon a star . . ."
2 Snake dance dancer
3 Scads
4 *Once Upon a* —
5 Terry Bradshaw, e.g.
6 Pomme de —
7 Collage
8 "The magic word"
9 The second A in "radar"
10 Popeye, e.g.
11 Assistant
12 Kilt feature
13 Get going
14 Twiddle thumbs
15 Gloomy
16 "Desire" orchard
26 Radioactive
27 TVA project
29 Harbor boat
32 Shoot the breeze
34 Two aspirin, often
35 Adam's arboretum
36 —-Lease Act
37 Born to the purple
38 Retain
40 Arbor Day honoree
41 Arab League member
42 Filmdom's bad guy George
45 Thole insert

47 Welsh rabbit base
50 Happily-after connection
52 Book of Mormon book
53 Landscaper's tool
58 Tomato blight
59 Yorkshire river
61 Overflow
62 Get going
64 Jalopy
66 Wanes
67 *ER* actor Wyle
68 Mrs. Copperfield
69 King David's predecessor
71 Lime cooler
72 Tried to beat the tag
73 *Clue* room
74 Perry's creator
77 — of mind

80 Wheeler-dealer
83 Egyptian snake
85 One more
88 Geologic time period
90 Dashiell's detective
91 Cleared the tape
93 Musical aptitude
95 Fakir's faith
97 *Siddhartha* author
98 Touch down
99 Yawl call
100 Lioness' lack
101 Akron product
103 Kin of collard greens
104 Bay
105 On bended —
106 FAX
109 Preschooler

# Puzzle 2-6: Three in a Row

## Across

1 Neck-and-neck
5 *The Clan of the Cave* —
9 Blowout
13 Betty Grable's asset
17 "Rule Britannia" composer
18 Scat queen Fitzgerald
19 Expanse
20 Camus setting
21 AAA
25 Tennis star Sampras
26 Emile Zola novel
27 Measure of garlic
28 Got up
31 Z — zebra
33 Black eye
34 OOO
39 *Jeopardy* host Trebek
40 Affectedly creative
41 "Every pot has its —"

42 Wt. Watcher's loss
45 *Roundabout* group
46 San — Obispo, CA
47 Tread
49 Type of pigeon?
51 Cozy spots
52 Italian bread?
53 Babyish remark
54 MMM
59 Exercises, as authority
60 Like Superman's vision
61 Pop of pop
62 Brainstorms
63 First victim
64 Yucatan years
65 Two-time U.S. Open champ
68 — Aviv
69 Yoko of rock
70 Libra's birthstone
71 Do magazine work

72 EEE
77 Ducks
80 "I don't —!"
81 Robert Fulton's power source
82 Singer Lopez
83 Gave a pink slip (to)
85 Computer fodder
87 XXX
94 *The — of Night*
95 Tolstoy heroine
96 Account entry
97 Coloratura Mills
98 Woodwind
99 Type of horse
100 1999 role for Cameron Diaz
101 Broker's advice

### Down

1 Run up a —
2 *Rosemary's Baby* author Levin
3 USNA grad
4 Jettison, slangily
5 Tuckered
6 *Vogue* competitor
7 *— My Children*
8 St. Louis pro
9 Split or peel
10 Presley's middle name
11 Antitoxins
12 Actor Holbrook
13 Ken Dryden, once
14 Gas in electric bulbs
15 A color purple
16 Nasty look
22 "— there, done that"
23 Letter before a name
24 Yodeler's answer
28 On the road
29 Stir up
30 Change for a fin
31 After John
32 The limit, often
33 Avg.
35 Gives a Bronx cheer
36 Notre Dame's Fighting —

37 Jerk's companion
38 Half a ton
42 Peacock, to NBC
43 Alternative to bust
44 Kind of gin
46 *Live at —* (1970 Who album)
47 Floor cover material
48 Butler's prop
49 Joni Mitchell output
50 Mrs. Thatcher, notably
51 Boxer Oscar — Hoya
52 Tackle box gear
53 *American —* (Richard Gere film)
54 Birdbrain
55 Skin
56 Projectionist's unit
57 *The — Incident*
58 Entertainer Shore
63 "Have you — wool?"
64 Church recess
65 Chanteuse Adams
66 Judy's daughter
67 Goblet holder
69 Where to find RNs
70 "— the ramparts . . ."
71 Beverly Hills homes
72 Sold
73 Guitarist Clapton
74 *The — Cometh* (Eugene O'Neill)
75 Pedestal part
76 "Como — usted?"
77 The heavens
78 Sultan's decree
79 Lament
83 Cartoonist Peter
84 Warrior princess of TV
85 Bambi and family
86 Type of ant
88 Henley participant
89 Vigor
90 "Give — rest!"
91 Pique
92 Zip
93 Hair-styling product

# Puzzle 2-7: You Bet!

## Across

1 Jerusalem's Mosque of —
5 Panhandler's income
9 Ribs, technically
13 Unveil
17 Type of model
18 "... where the buffalo —"
19 From square one
20 Part of BTU
21 Pre-storm forecast
22 Auctioneer's final word
23 Mitchell mansion
24 Outfit for Ben-Hur
25 "You bet!"
28 Confidential
30 Hoopster's target
31 Mrs. Dick Tracy
33 Phone button
34 "Yakety Yak" singers, after "The"
39 Below Greenwich Village
41 They go with pains
45 Stud's hangout
46 *Peter Pan* pet
48 — to a turn (perfect)
50 Give the boot
51 *A Chorus Line* number
52 Battle cry
54 Sound of reproach
55 Celestial beast
56 Date of birth, e.g.
58 Begets
60 Appetizer
62 Tuck's companion
64 Cod — oil
66 Roll call notation
67 Wrap tightly
71 Thumb or pinky
73 Rover's restraint
77 Southernmost US city
78 Shade tree
80 1987 Kim Basinger film
82 Spanish waterway
83 Beginning of Caesar's question
84 "Woe is me"
86 Singer Horne
87 Occupy
88 Yemen, once
90 "Heavens!"
92 Split up
94 Gratuity
96 Wyle of *ER*
98 Great Lakes cargo
99 Unleash

103 "You bet!"
109 Roman poet
110 Head of France
112 Mercyhurst College city
113 Jilt
114 Chutzpah
115 Author Murdoch
116 Weather phenomenon, with "El"
117 Toast topper
118 Kind of child
119 Grimm beginning
120 Mideast gulf
121 Shed

## Down

1 *Jaws* boat
2 Lot's son
3 "— fair in love ..."
4 Compunction
5 Debate
6 Joe Orton play
7 Big hair
8 Trout's cousin
9 Grain of porridge
10 Kodak moment
11 Dried-up
12 Tony or Oscar
13 "You bet!"
14 Any day
15 Baryshnikov's birthplace
16 List shortener
26 Ignited
27 "You bet!"
29 Pirate's place
32 Turf
34 Hopper introduction
35 Mrs. Chaplin
36 Drive the getaway car
37 "Dang!"
38 Slow pace-setter
40 Blame
42 Mary Beth or William
43 "— quam videri" (North Carolina motto)
44 Alpha Centauri, for one
47 Bitter
49 James of jazz
52 In the throng
53 McHale of the Celtics
57 "You bet!"
59 *Oliver's Story* author
61 Ready, willing, and —
63 Negotiate a sentence, with "bargain"
65 Disney World attractions

**67** *Take Her, — Mine*
**68** Together
**69** Der — (Adenauer nickname)
**70** *Vogue* rival
**72** Prong
**74** Tebaldi tune
**75** Delta deposit
**76** Bagel feature
**79** Attractive
**81** Patisserie treat
**85** — Paolo, Brazil
**87** Another word for "nothing left to lose"
**89** Ventilate
**91** Use a hanky
**93** Pitcher's pride

**95** Barbecue setting
**97** Serengeti sight
**99** Brand identity
**100** Lendl of tennis
**101** It gets rung up
**102** Sea swallow
**104** Like the Sahara
**105** Hook-sinker connection
**106** First name in folk
**107** Coward of note
**108** Fido's friend
**111** Computer add-on

# Puzzle 2-8: S-Sandwich

**HINT**

Take the title literally in this theme!

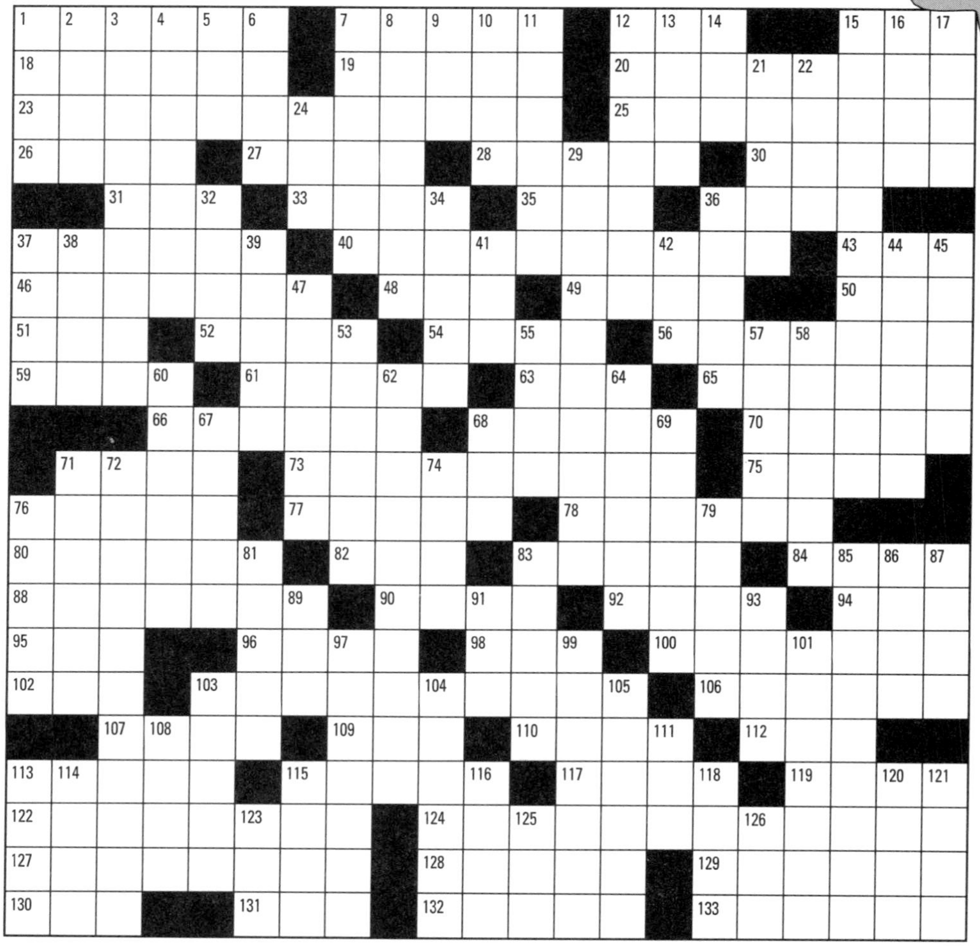

[Crossword grid with numbered squares: 1–133]

## Across

1 Christopher Plummer's daughter
7 Toward the stern
12 Provide weapons
15 Charlton Heston film, with *El*
18 — the boom (gets serious)
19 Maison room
20 Chopin work
23 Part of a marching band
25 Kind of committee
26 Prepare the laundry
27 "— a Song Go Out of My Heart"
28 Finnish lake
30 What a baseball player may steal
31 Whitney or Wallach
33 Was hip (to)

35 International softball org.
36 OED offerings
37 Truffaut's field
40 Tuxedo go-with
43 AARP members
46 May birthstone
48 Canine cry
49 The jaguarundi
50 Like Willie Winkie
51 Connections
52 Cooking direction
54 Charlie Brown remark
56 Stick in the envelope
59 Came in second
61 Thin as —
63 Computer key

65 Looked daggers at
66 Religious contrariness
68 A female demon
70 "— a Man" (Willingham)
71 Anna of silent films
73 Playing fields for Bobby Fischer
75 Kiln
76 Composer Copland
77 "Nothing — excited about"
78 In the pool
80 Baby piano
82 Wright wing?
83 Beaver's kin
84 Monumental
88 Soothe
90 Get an — effort
92 Killer whale
94 Honshu bay
95 Screen star Gibson
96 Word for Yorick
98 Lee of filmdom (*The Ice Storm*)
100 Rudimentary
102 Summer cooler
103 Wahine wear
106 24-hour eateries
107 God of love
109 Part of the school cal.
110 Tender
112 Medicare grp.
113 Confused
115 Fabled fabler
117 "Auld Lang —"
119 — dixit
122 One of five in ballet
124 Problem for Cinderella
127 Makes the sofa bed
128 Venetian's vest
129 Took out the Sunfish
130 Singer O'Connor
131 "— my party and I'll cry . . ."
132 2000 and 2001
133 Church leaders

## Down

1 Papal vestments
2 Philippine Muslim
3 Sensibility
4 Like a baby bird
5 *ER* types
6 Holly plant
7 Climb
8 Walkman's power source
9 Ring king
10 Arctic sight
11 Sampras' game
12 Mob rule
13 Went by limo
14 Twelfth-century date
15 Duel

16 Regarding
17 Algerian rulers
21 Nepal's neighbor
22 Mil. branch
24 Lodge member
29 Rating
32 "— corny as Kansas . . ."
34 Unnerving
36 Sturm's partner
37 Overlay
38 — *Angel* (Mae West)
39 Rite site
41 Type of cuisine
42 Dander
44 Serve as usher again
45 Origins
47 Emulate 98 Across
53 Attend to Dobbin's hoof
55 Leaves in a cup
57 Athenian demagogue
58 Hairy, as a plant
60 "This is dedicated to — I love"
62 Specs
64 *Opere* — (in the work quoted)
67 Nine combiner
68 WWII landing craft
69 Fall blooms
71 Spent
72 Theme of this puzzle
74 Woman's magazine
76 Japanese volcano
79 Made a bow
81 Russian rulers, once
83 Avifauna
85 Hawaiian export
86 River to the Danube
87 Animation frames
89 Guido's note
91 Former acorn
93 Author Martin (*London Fields*)
97 Nods
99 More unappetizing
101 Dull
103 Tin can nibblers
104 Like the L.A. sky, perhaps
105 Agreed-upon meetings
108 Check
111 Printing measures
113 Like an amoeba
114 Keep on swigging
115 Juillet follower
116 Ballerina's bend
118 Ultimatum word
120 Psychic
121 Cockney flocks
123 — *Dalmatians*
125 Pie-mode connector
126 Adjectival suffix

# Puzzle 2-9: As They Say

The Libran birthstone of 1 Across is a luminescent gem.

## Across

1 Libran birthstone
5 Companion to hearty
9 "Out, Puss!"
13 Over with
17 Walk to and fro
18 Sits in the cellar
19 Peregrinate
20 Vega —, PR
21 French I verb
22 Sargasso, etc.
23 Gregory Peck thriller, with *The*
24 *General Hospital*, for one
25 Talk, as they say
28 Word with cooker
30 Usher's support
31 Shout
33 Preschooler
34 Tote
39 "A friend in — . . ."
41 Wall Street unit
45 Still sleeping
46 ". . . where the buffalo — . . ."
48 "Basta!"
50 Coleridge contemporary
51 Bloodshot
52 Peggy Fleming, e.g.
54 Time frame
55 Length of fabric
56 Five and ten cent —
58 Frighten off
60 Meeting record
62 Meal opener
64 Fit for a king
66 Sleepy's comrade
67 Ghost
71 Little Bighorn, e.g.
73 Jolly Roger image
77 Anatolian
78 Where to find Sugarloaf
80 Strict
82 DC group
83 Spew
84 "No way!"
86 Weather phenomenon, with "El"
87 Chester Arthur's middle name
88 "— Man"
90 Backyard sight
92 Poors' companion
94 Goof
96 Harvest
98 Divot

99 Board game
103 Act prematurely, as they say
109 Albuquerque student
110 Old-fashioned do?
112 Hamlet or Romeo
113 Letters from space
114 Populous place
115 Prime the pot
116 Garble
117 Count calories
118 Left, on the map
119 Where deliveries are made
120 O'Neill orchard
121 To boot

## Down

1 Cartel since 1960
2 Down the beaten —
3 Farm division
4 — Islands
5 Service stripe
6 Cockeyed
7 Table extension
8 Test format
9 Like a Michigan football game
10 Finished
11 State
12 Palindromic principle
13 Blame others, as they say
14 Baseball family
15 Christmas-tree topper
16 First-aid kit item
26 Sample
27 Countdown start
29 1975 Abba hit
32 Bandleader Baxter
34 Indy entries
35 Encourage
36 Upgrade
37 Insert ammo
38 "Ciao"
40 Harvard housing
42 Scads
43 Tick off
44 Truck stop sign
47 39.37 inches
49 Invoice stamp
52 Ticket information
53 Kathie Lee cohost
57 Make waves, as they say
59 Baltimore gridder
61 Smoke detector?

63 Beach bird
65 Weekend wear
67 Cherry leftover
68 Mountain lion
69 Author Ambler
70 Laugh-provoking time
72 Flat fee?
74 Home of the Bruins, for short
75 Perjurer
76 Get, as the job
79 Lehar format
81 Chicken displays
85 Arizona to Kansas dir.
87 Postscripts
89 Planet

91 — Mahal
93 Okayama drama
95 Colonel Potter's man
97 Prize money
99 Bear — (pastry)
100 New York state flower
101 Sacred bird of the Pharaohs
102 Evaporated
104 Flanders of fiction
105 Prune, once
106 Sprinter Devers
107 Depletes, with "up"
108 Treaty org.
111 Part of HRH

# Puzzle 2-10: Vive Irma La Douce and Friends

Another clue for 26 Across is "Hertz rival."

## Across

1 Drubbing
5 Kerouac's "generation," for example
9 Bamako's country
13 Funny Wilson
17 Anglo-Saxon serf
18 An avatar of Vishnu
19 Flamingo, often
20 One of a Sleeping Beauty trio
21 Shirley MacLaine film with Twiggy (1988)
24 Type of Greek verse or architecture
25 Turkish weight
26 Rara —
27 "That's right"
28 Georgia O'Keeffe, e.g.
29 Former inmate
31 *Vanity* —
32 Essences

34 Shirley's film debut via Hitchcock (1955)
40 Speaker's place
41 Lean (on)
42 Sheltered
43 Grimace
44 Variety of shark
45 Type of rock
47 Canned heat
49 Springsteen's birthplace?
50 Hydrogen's number
51 Coward and others
52 Flushing field
53 Runner Bannister
55 Cowboys' gear
57 Shirley film with Nicolas Cage
60 School credit
61 Crossword elements
62 Measure of paint

63 Shirley film with Chita Rivera (1969)
67 Off-the-mark noun
71 Ruffled
72 Actor Barry *(War of the Worlds)*
73 Where bowlers meet
74 *Kojiki* author
75 Rocky peak
76 Recitatives
79 Top of the Pops output
80 *Billy* — (Melville)
81 Enceladus' burial place
83 Word of woe
84 Brownie point
85 Gal from Glasgow
86 Shirley MacLaine film with Carol Kane (1971)
91 "It's a bird, it's a — . . ."
92 Do modern surgery
93 Moves like a clod
96 Where Noah landed
99 Posted
100 Winsor McKay cartoon character
101 Meadow
102 Guide
103 Shirley MacLaine film with Frank Sinatra (1958)
107 Gothic arch element
108 Revile
109 Curse, with "eye"
110 Cost of cards
111 Take out
112 Quote
113 Diplomacy
114 Robert Stack TV role

## Down

1 Do the floor over
2 City on Honshu Bay
3 Agreed to do
4 Social event
5 Military commission
6 Less onerous
7 Israeli novelist Oz
8 St. Anthony's cross
9 Ready for picking
10 Woodworking tool
11 Albanian currency
12 A Gershwin
13 Jetsam's partner
14 TV actress Anderson
15 Rainbow goddess
16 International treaty
19 With caution
20 Moray or Solway, e.g.
22 Stag party attendees
23 Groom's place
28 Unhealthy pallor

30 Miami River locale
31 Adds zest (to)
32 *Balm in —*
33 Roman road
35 Oxford student's hurdle
36 Tends the garden
37 Blusher
38 Tricks
39 *The Best — of Our Lives*
40 *Wayne's World* regular
44 Puzo subject, with "the"
45 Type of boom
46 British PM before Wilson
47 Questionable
48 Body parts
51 Edict of — (Huguenot decree of 1598)
52 Fancy hotel digs
54 Conductor Klemperer
56 Two voices as one
57 Looks sheepish
58 Cake finisher
59 Snoops
61 Travolta musical
63 Located
64 Followed Jane Austen
65 Brings home the bacon
66 Related through Dad
67 Rough-textured blanket
68 Sheer fabric
69 Some are offensive
70 Colleague of Paddy
73 Setting for 51 Down
77 Jeweler's weight
78 Pizzazz
79 Type of daisy
80 Cutting remark
82 Greenlight
84 "Monopoly" deck
85 Soft drink garnish
87 Make joyful
88 Mr. Fawlty
89 Man of the cloth
90 Uprising
94 Landlord's income
95 Wise men
96 Amoeba, famously
97 Birthplace of Baryshnikov
98 Dismounted
99 X-rated material
100 Winter Palace river
103 Cul-de-—
104 Cummerbund in Kyoto
105 Bumped into
106 Grey of "Three Smart Girls"

# Puzzle 2-11: Word Travels

## Across

1 Word on a lighted street sign
5 Pedal pushers
9 How word travels for 33 cents
13 Dupe
17 Seaman's term
18 Political duck
19 *Sesame Street* giggler
20 World Cup sensation
21 Getz of jazz
22 One of *The Waltons*
23 Pew
24 Home of the Fighting Christians
25 How word traveled in the Old West
28 Where you get charley horses
30 *Exodus* hero
31 Wear's partner
33 Freudian —
34 Tease
37 The basics
40 Develops
42 Search engine
45 Nabokov heroine
46 Was bumped off
48 Rabbit features
50 — Linda, CA
51 Swoon
53 Lab burners
55 Castle's defense
57 The puck stops here
58 Caesar or Waldorf
60 Start to drop
62 Collard —
64 How word travels by air
68 Shakespearean hero
71 One of the King Sisters
72 Olympics symbol
76 Potential perch
77 No-see-um
80 Brunch course
82 One and only
83 Baby powder
85 Dutch export
87 Mubarak's predecessor
89 Augusta score
90 Bric-a-brac place
92 Thames town
94 Office communique
95 She sheep
96 Overdrive
98 Shortly
100 Chicago-to-Detroit dir.

102 World Series champs of 1979
105 How word travels upward
111 OPEC member
112 Mohair maker
114 — carotene
115 Subject for Fellini
116 Waiter's income
117 Ruth's *Laugh-In* co-star
118 Plumbing problem
119 Ad infinitum
120 *Off the Court* author
121 Sinister look
122 First name in modeling
123 Vat

## Down

1 John Cheever prototype
2 Chorus girl
3 Fat-free
4 *Out of Africa* setting
5 Elastic
6 Tombstone marshal
7 Desert dignitary
8 Basic belief
9 Final word, perhaps
10 Toby jug contents
11 Mosque official
12 Yoga position
13 Blue plate —
14 How word travels in 1999
15 Kitchen plant
16 Second part of YMCA
26 Edwardian and Elizabethan
27 Red or Black
29 Stallone's nickname
32 Paper quantity
34 NFC team
35 Light bulb, to Popeye
36 Cotillion
38 Pamper, with "to"
39 Mideast peninsula
41 Sellout letters
43 Tip-off
44 Porridge
47 Type of orange
49 Stuffing seasoning
52 Snack in Saltillo
54 Emergency room item
56 Turkey —
59 "Rats!"
61 Moles
63 Slaughter of baseball

**65** The Cubs' Sandberg
**66** Belief of 11 Down
**67** Hollow rock
**68** Companion of crafts
**69** Yannick of the courts
**70** How word travels by wire
**73** Tug-of-war material
**74** Talon
**75** Head count reply
**78** Gator chaser
**79** "Later!"
**81** Junior, for example
**84** Sanitize
**86** "— Mash"
**88** Nobelist Morrison

**91** Jack Sprat's no-no
**93** Nice name
**97** Buick model
**99** High born
**101** Everglades bird
**102** Hummus holder
**103** Spring bloom
**104** Miffed
**106** On an even —
**107** Common catchall
**108** PBS program
**109** Sunday sign-off
**110** Escapade
**113** Sampled the sushi

# Puzzle 2-12: What's Playing at the Forum?

 Roman numerals are popular in puzzles, as per the theme of this puzzle.

[Crossword grid]

## Across

1 Middle name at Graceland
5 Dance step
11 Attempt
15 Type of exam
19 Event at Macy's
20 Like many a country lane
21 "Fame" singer Irene
22 Sweet beginning
23 Charlton Heston epic of 1956
26 Hawkeye portrayer
27 Radioactive particle
28 "I'm a — Doodle Dandy . . ."
29 Unfocused look
30 Sikh's topper

34 *The — and the Pendulum*
35 Rabbit of fiction
36 Jack Nicholson film of 1970
41 — Rica
44 Staff at *GQ*
45 Garfield's pal
46 *The — of the Iguana*
48 Argentine river
50 Classroom paint
54 Tractor maker
56 Fret over
60 Storing, as feed
62 Lancaster-Douglas thriller of 1964
64 Validate
66 Pub fixtures
67 English Channel feeder

**68** A Kennedy
**71** Fido's tormentors
**73** Discourage
**76** Nancy Drew's boyfriend
**77** Iowa society
**80** Gulf of the Ionian Sea
**82** Removes the water
**85** Disney remake of 1996
**89** Admitted to the order
**93** Laborious work
**94** Undo the wedding vows
**96** — deprivation
**97** Boardwalk regulars
**99** Put off
**101** Mex. miss
**102** Wanted poster init.
**105** Donnybrook
**107** Henry Fonda film of 1957
**111** Maggie Smith and Judi Dench
**113** DC type
**115** "Surfin' —" (Beach Boys 1962 hit)
**116** Soviet lake
**117** Breadwinner
**120** Servitude of olde
**125** *Eyeless in* — (Aldous Huxley)
**126** Oliver Reed–Raquel Welch film of 1974
**130** Harrow challenger
**131** Alaskan outpost
**132** Redeem
**133** Habeas corpus, e.g.
**134** Transmit
**135** "The — have it!" (result of 36 Down)
**136** Indian and Arctic
**137** Word with dial

## Down

**1** Wine center of Italy
**2** Pompom girls' cries
**3** Believe it's not butter
**4** Word at the sandwich counter
**5** Appear
**6** Shoulder-elbow links
**7** Where to use a PIN
**8** B & O stop
**9** 68 Across, for one
**10** Whirlpool
**11** Type of overlook
**12** Summer shirt
**13** "Verrry interesting" comedian Johnson
**14** Off — (mistaken)
**15** Variety of orange
**16** Tell the tale
**17** Impressed
**18** Drivers, to Barry Bonds
**24** French statesman René
**25** Chart
**31** Big — (London landmark)
**32** Sarcastic
**33** Desert of Israel

**35** Creole dialect
**36** Cast a ballot
**37** Land west of Nod
**38** Sets one's sights
**39** Like an old-time photo
**40** Role for Valentino
**42** Do in the dragon
**43** Labels
**47** Had a go
**49** *Green Gables* girl
**51** Santa's helper
**52** Clapton solo, e.g.
**53** Blue dye
**55** Barely won
**57** "— the Mood For Love"
**58** Author Grey
**59** Gawked at
**61** "— Caesar's ghost!"
**63** Jeff Bagwell, e.g.
**65** *West Side Story* heroine
**68** Sensitivity
**69** Bedouin bigwig
**70** Tzara's art movement
**72** — *and Deliver*
**74** Dumbo's outstanding features
**75** Take the taxi
**78** Church area
**79** Sirens
**81** Tack on
**83** Society lady Kempner
**84** *Carrie* portrayer Spacek
**86** Hot pants relation
**87** Emcee Trebek
**88** Moslem mystics
**90** *Cheers* patron
**91** Art Deco illustrator
**92** Cannon of film
**95** Role for Carrie Fisher
**98** — Court
**100** WW II fliers
**102** Sayings
**103** *The — Kid*
**104** Warrior woman
**106** Settles, with "up"
**108** Serviette
**109** Salad component
**110** Rise up
**112** Antelope
**114** Hawaiian garland
**117** Lab burner
**118** Cry from the crow's nest
**119** *Little Caesar* gangster
**121** Gingrich nickname
**122** Space introduction
**123** Say "cheese"
**124** Italian Renaissance family
**127** Fleetwood —
**128** Take advantage of
**129** — Na Na

# Puzzle 2-13: Vanishing Acts

### Across

1 Endured
6 Domestic doyenne Stewart
12 Rebel, with "up"
15 Fannie —
18 With 4 Down, famed diarist
19 Turkish massif
20 A Stooge
21 Aces at the Olympics
22 Vanishing act?
24 Fifth, e.g.
25 Wife of Osiris
26 Author Rand
27 German painter Nolde
28 Photo finish
30 Struck, Biblically
31 Jordan's neighbor
33 Vanishing act?
36 Give evidence
38 Athlete from L.A.
39 Deli order
40 Pirate's treasure

41 Teatime treat
43 Wrist-elbow connector
46 "—! In The Name Of Love"
49 Vanishing act?
53 Weather map indications
55 Anti-smoking lobby
56 Belief
57 Forever
58 Hippy shape?
60 Jordan's capital
62 Sgt. Snorkel's dog
63 Hawthorne town
65 Parisian river
66 Vanishing act?
73 Come up
74 *Waiting for* — (Odets)
75 Cecilia Bartoli solo
76 Spanish soprano — Lorengar
77 Type size
78 "To err is — . . ."
80 Go downhill?
83 Psychic power

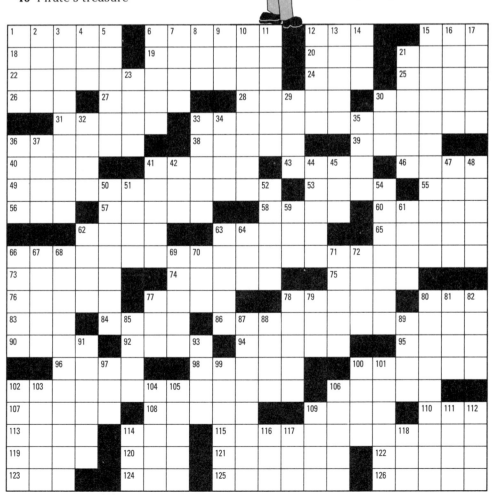

84 Place for a coin
86 Vanishing act?
90 Stops on the B & O
92 Inspiration
94 Evangelist McPherson
95 Like Silver's rider
96 Newsbreak
98 Stately home
100 Rang
102 Vanishing act?
106 Plumed water bird
107 The Jetsons' pet
108 Drying ovens
109 Fall flat
110 Sandbank
113 Streak
114 — man out
115 Vanishing act?
119 Astrophysicist Penzias
120 Announcement word
121 Girlish nicknames
122 Knock one's socks off
123 Thanksgiving dinner request
124 Dated
125 Takes the bait
126 River through Rome

## Down

1 Rum dessert
2 Without siblings
3 April forecast
4 See 18 Across
5 Sand and gravel drifts
6 Peter Maas subject
7 Syr Darya's outflow
8 Kurosawa epic
9 Crowd, in Capri
10 Swinging blow
11 Sergeant's command
12 Big name in violins
13 Sorority for Sabrina?
14 Tiger's prop
15 Early seat of civilization
16 *Fraud* novelist Brookner
17 German steel center
21 Kitchen gadgets
23 Overlook
29 Word on a st. sign
30 Haggard novel
32 Himalayan hulk
33 Acts like the Don
34 "Daily Planet" report Lois

35 Turn liquid
36 Russian range
37 A-one
41 Vibrated
42 Take for a ride?
44 Beast of Bolivia
45 Scand. nation
47 Muscat denizen
48 Game show folks
50 Adds shampoo
51 Bristle
52 Spread out, as toes
54 Giving the business
59 Sargasso "serpent"
61 Physical introduction
62 Bones, anatomically
63 Castro showroom items
64 Place for a rudder
66 Portable albums
67 Hand-arm connector
68 Monet's "Blue Water Lilies," e.g.
69 Crème de la crème
70 Word on a wine bottle
71 Ike's Mrs.
72 Breakfast cereal
77 Where peas dwell
78 Four-base hit?
79 Shoshonean nomad
80 Southern seafood specialty
81 Batman's creator
82 Provoked
85 South American capital
87 Tall, dark, and —
88 Where the Aisne ends
89 Neatnik's nightmare
91 Camp cooker
93 Israeli novelist Oz
97 Tokyo, once
99 Pollen producer
100 Campus VIP
101 Jazz aficionado
102 Part of USNA
103 River past Grenoble
104 Alpine call
105 Stepped into the waves
106 Lipstick alternative
109 Get cold — (chicken out)
111 Woodworking tool
112 Flanders river
114 Lennon's lady
116 Thurman of *Pulp Fiction*
117 Bracketed word
118 Friend of Francois

# Puzzle 2-14: Animal Families

When you see the phrase "and family" in a clue, you're looking at a plural entry.

## Across

1 Desert shrub
7 Antilles native
12 More daring
18 Epic poem
19 Comfort
20 Kicked back
22 Marsh bird and family
24 So-so
25 Fatima's husband
26 Like a Lee Majors character
27 Self-possession
29 Encountered
30 Actor Kingsley and others
32 Crossword's slave
33 Ram's pride
35 Possessive word
36 Proficient
38 Babar and family
42 Bireme propeller
44 Red or Dead
45 First *King Kong* girl
46 "I kid you not!"
47 High-powered attorney, e.g.
51 Used a Cuisinart
53 Horse's hue
54 Memorable time
55 Nerdy one
57 Postal creed connector
58 Tailless cat
59 Vampire —
62 Billy and family
65 Auctioneer's last word
66 Florentine river
67 Greets the judge
68 *M*A*S*H* milieu
69 Sign of hunger
70 Vexed
71 Where to put the dough
72 Unit of thunder
73 Belligerent bird and family
75 Took the first step
76 "What happened —?"
77 Word with tote or school
78 Israeli folk dance
79 Denial in Dundee
80 Like the Sahara
81 Philippine general
83 Crab claws
85 Coins

88 Harmless cyst
89 Computer language
91 Afternoon meal
92 South Dakota state bird and family
96 Spring bloom
100 Disagreeable obligation
101 French coastal town
102 "Pop — the weasel!"
104 Unescorted
105 Mythical bird
106 Purple shade
108 Small jewelry case
110 Pink-slip
111 Joy
113 Felix and family
117 VIP entourage
118 Rich desserts
119 Bridge of Venice
120 Intuited
121 Asparagus unit
122 Make beloved

## Down

1 Winter melon
2 Well-— (elegant)
3 Giraudoux drama
4 Turkey dinner request
5 Fail the polygraph
6 Hacienda material
7 In a bind
8 Russian range
9 — *Notorious* (Marlene Dietrich film)
10 Driving hazard
11 Make the bed, old style
12 Stew, as vegetables
13 Speeds, with "up"
14 To shelter
15 Crossword tag for alt. spelling
16 Look at closely
17 College officials
19 Tea time treats
21 Cannot stomach
23 School members?
28 — child
31 Name on a doghouse
34 Put on the market
35 *Magic Mountain* author
37 Dances, in Argentina
39 Fragile

40 "— home" *(ET)*
41 Scam
43 Reduce sails
47 Esso product
48 Hit the big time
49 Brought up
50 Welcomed heartily
52 — Cob, CT
53 Burmese capital
56 Sacred text
58 Lunar unit
59 Rock singer Jackson
60 French Benedictine Saint
61 Discards
63 Sword's challenger
64 Unit of elec.
65 The US version of 47 Down
66 Palindromic constellation
69 Eastern temple
70 "Goin' to the —, and we're gonna get married . . ."
72 The C in CEO
73 Rotating piece
74 Glassmaking material

76 The Bee Gees, famously
77 Everyday
80 Good serves
81 Sends back to Congress
82 Warbler
84 Beach toy
85 Noisy sleeper
86 Mexican parched-corn flours
87 Teach a lesson (to)
88 Congressional member
90 Fuels the flames
93 Leveled out
94 Safe and sound
95 Psychic friend?
97 Setting
98 Buddhist doctrine
99 X-rating giver
103 Mall attraction
106 Wins at rummy
107 Bounder
109 Princess in *A Bug's Life*
112 Type of ear?
114 Trim a tree
115 Half a sawbuck
116 See 107 Down

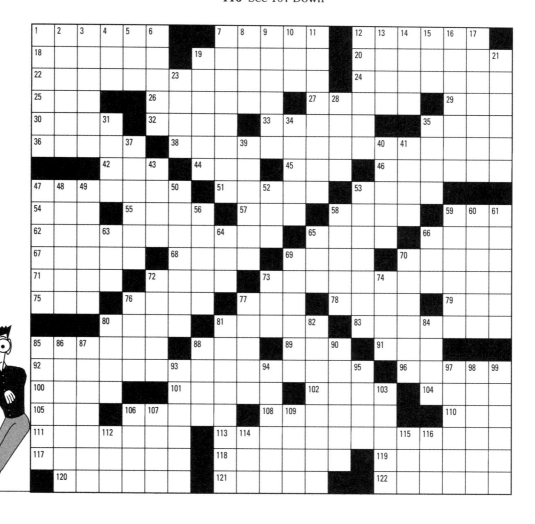

# Puzzle 2-15: The Y Factor

## Across

1 Tipper's man
7 Like the Lhasa apso
14 Most wise
20 Pipe smoker's gadget
21 — exception (almost never)
22 Captivate
23 Four-time Daytona 500 winner
25 North American elk
26 Unwritten
27 Polly and others
28 Gilbert and Sullivan princess
30 Babe's breakfast
31 Tinker-Chance middleman
34 Uses a scope
37 Earlier than the present
39 Steak order
42 START II treaty signatory
48 After zeta
49 Explorer John or actor Sebastian
52 Mudville complement
53 Pipe cleaner?
54 Green land
56 Rector's income
58 In short supply
61 Incites, with "on"
62 She played Jennifer on *Family Ties*
65 Ivy league school founder
67 "— la vista, baby!"
68 Gives off
70 Persnickety people
71 Step on it
74 Get going
76 Charles, to Elizabeth
77 Delectable mollusk
81 Color of honey
83 "— all, folks!" (cartoon sign-off)
88 "All in the Family" co-producer
91 "Puff the Magic Dragon" group member
94 Jerry's straight man
95 Belief of over a billion
97 Calf-catching event
98 Novelist O'Brien
99 Blyton and namesakes
101 "Peek-—!"
103 Knotty situation
105 Polo Grounds legend
106 *The Farmer's Daughter* star
110 Collectible figurines
112 Chew the fat
113 Teddy
114 Broom — (comic strip witch)
115 Speaker in Cooperstown

119 — *culpa*
121 Old Scratch
123 "— Lama Ding Dong"
127 One of the Finger Lakes
129 "Where Your Road Leads" singer
134 Type of cracker
135 Make unnecessary
136 Grosse —, MI
137 Hang up one's cleats, e.g.
138 Noxious atmospheres
139 Beliefs

## Down

1 — Arena
2 Jet-setter's jet
3 Big bash
4 Brunch order
5 Actor Alejandro or Fernando
6 Historic time
7 Forbidden things
8 "Time — My Side" (Rolling Stones hit)
9 Toper's debt
10 What glaciers cause
11 Greek cross
12 S.A. country
13 Radar O'Reilly's drink
14 Type of plant?
15 Santa —, CA
16 Chasms
17 Jannings of *The Blue Angel*
18 — speak (as it were)
19 Journey
24 Welsh —
29 Hudson's *Pillow Talk* co-star
32 Short holiday?
33 Poetic muse
35 Med. scanners
36 "— I Fell For You"
38 Over the hill
39 Comb parts
40 Courtyards
41 Cats and dogs, sometimes
43 Jesse Ventura, once
44 Deuce toppers
45 Long tales
46 Fireplace
47 Snoops
50 "Top — mornin'!"
51 "— fightin' words!"
55 Rebellious Turner
57 *Fear of Flying* author

**59** Small shots
**60** "Comin' — the Rye"
**63** *Gulliver's Travels* brute
**64** Off-Broadway dance show
**66** Mountains of Utah
**69** Like a judge?
**72** Calvary inscription
**73** Mousy remarks
**75** Grand —
**77** Gamal — Nasser
**78** Wimbledon champ Maria
**79** Oil-fire fighter Red
**80** Paul of *Hollywood Squares*
**82** Take from the top
**84** Charlemagne's domain: abbr.
**85** Passionate interest
**86** Kemo Sabe's sidekick
**87** Flattens a fly
**89** *As — Dying* (William Faulkner)
**90** Mover and shaker
**92** Discriminate against, in mortgage granting
**93** "— pay for this!"

**96** Pout
**100** Dirty digs
**102** Successor to Kennedy
**104** Bummed
**107** Tijuana treat
**108** Mimic
**109** Type of cracker
**111** *Origin of Species* author
**114** Helen of stage
**115** Winter Palace resident
**116** Artist Magritte
**117** "What's — for me?"
**118** Long-haul vehicle
**120** Positron's place
**122** Hanky-waver's word
**124** Top-notch
**125** Apple juice maker
**126** Sidewalk-stand drinks
**128** Kia
**130** Stat for Ken Griffey, Jr.
**131** Given name for Tokyo Rose
**132** Suitable
**133** Wade's courtroom opponent

# Puzzle 2-16: Around the Monopoly Board

## Across

1 Kiss and tell
5 Oliver Twist's request
9 Harvard housing
13 Hoodwink
17 Where the Liffey flows
18 City outside Des Moines
19 Brainstorming session upshot
20 Computer key
21 Like Darth Vader
22 Spiffy
23 Word with "short" or "suit"
24 Jane Austen novel
25 Monopoly mode of travel
29 Old-time TV show "The — Squad"
30 Length x width
31 Happy Meal bonus
32 Shaka, e.g.
34 Hue and cry
37 Pig chaser
38 Proof
42 Like granola
43 "Mayday!"

44 Caught in the act
45 Monster of the desert
46 Vinaigrette ingredient
47 Pointer
48 *Wall — Journal*
50 Howard Carter's discovery
51 Jeremiah Johnson, e.g.
54 Lead, as a meeting
55 "Shaft" composer Isaac
57 *High —*
58 Onerous task
59 Pear
60 Utility, with "works"
62 Toil
63 Matt Dillon, for one
66 Poetic pugilist
67 *The Great —*
69 Witty one
70 Freudian interest
71 Wedding day shower?
73 First name in fairy tales
74 Recipe instruction

75 Helium, etc.
77 Gregarious blackbird
79 Groupie
80 Fancy hotel digs
81 Copper Mountain resort
82 Expose
83 Fly high
84 Female kangaroo
86 Monopoly power source
93 Sigmund's daughter
95 Matinee —
96 Ginza glow
97 Cairo's river
98 Missile in the Gulf War
99 Three squared
100 To be, to Henri
101 Grammy category
102 Listen to
103 Kelly of *An American in Paris*
104 Tea leaf reader
105 Preschooler

## Down

1 Ballpark beverage
2 Learn's partner
3 Tebaldi tune
4 Crone
5 Demeanor
6 Zee, to Zeus
7 "Step to the — of the bus!"
8 Beverly Hills homes
9 Like some pickles
10 Reputation
11 Clinton cabinet member
12 *TV Guide,* for one
13 That girl
14 Monopoly deck
15 Caisson's contents
16 Anthropologist Margaret
26 Remove wrinkles
27 Cyclotron particle
28 Washout
33 Part of a journey
34 Moorhen's cousin

35 Sanctum
36 Monopoly property
37 Mom's partner
38 Unnerving
39 Avoid a crash
40 Game with Professor Plum
41 Hash house sign
43 Title for Elton John
44 Lock eyes
47 Part of a royal flush
48 Depart, with "off"
49 Skipper of the Kon-Tiki
52 "Annabel Lee" poet
53 Read
54 Rodeo wear
56 Halfwit
58 Trolley signal
59 Diamond corner
60 Part of VFW
61 Deplaned
62 See 53 Down
63 — Factor
64 Off-kilter
65 At a — for words
68 Coin, for Dickens
69 Take the gold
72 Roaring Twenties, e.g.
74 "Tell it to the —"
75 Island discovered by Magellan
76 Arthur Hailey novel
78 Commit perjury
79 Douglas, for one
80 Norman student
82 Seed seller W. — Burpee
83 Twenty
84 Smidgen
85 As soon as
87 Newswoman Magnus
88 Boxer Billy
89 Group of badgers
90 Sailor's word
91 Actor Nolte
92 Harness the oxen
94 Make sense, with "up"

# Puzzle 2-17: Two For Tee

## Across

1 Grammy category
4 "Stranger — fiction"
8 Four-poster
11 Bruce Wayne's alter ego
17 Altar phrase
18 Playwright David
19 "— Believer" (Monkees' hit)
20 Each
21 Playground equipment
24 Antisocial ones
25 Star of Scorpius
26 1985 Best Actor winner
27 Jalopies
28 Apple pie go-with?
29 Navy rival
30 — the Hoople (60s rockers)
31 Inches
34 Type of gin
35 A — of the Circus (John Irving novel)
36 The Beehive State
40 A.k.a. Hollywood
42 The — We Were (Barbra Streisand film)
43 Wander
44 Joseph's is colorful
45 Galena, e.g.
46 The Cat in the —
47 Tick off
48 After FDR
49 1990 Broadway one-man show
50 Band of pirates?
52 Barber's tools
53 "She sells seashells," for one
56 Early Stephen King thriller
59 Skinny as a string —
60 Branch
61 Place for a spread
64 Located along a line
65 Wolfman portrayer Chaney
66 Pie-mode link
67 Sharpen
68 Sweet introduction
69 Pasture
70 In disarray
73 Lord Anthony
74 What an IRA earns
75 Actress Perlman of "Cheers"
76 Stockpile
77 Temporary colors
79 Chews the fat
80 "— Sera, Sera"
81 Pottery remnants
84 Gallimaufry
85 Tequila —
89 Before hair spray
90 Kellogg's character
92 Delphi priest
93 Pique
94 Muskrat's kin
95 Earthy prefix
96 Lost intentionally
97 Isr. neighbor
98 Auctioneer's cry
99 1998-99, e.g.

## Down

1 Beatles' meter maid
2 M´iddle Eastern gulf
3 Ted Hughes, e.g.
4 Bette Midler movie of 1979
5 Seraglio
6 Part of BA
7 Darwinism lead-in
8 Asphalt component
9 Manicurist's board
10 Devon river
11 Setting for Juliet
12 To the left, nautically
13 "What's Love Got to Do With It" vocalist
14 Wrestling match
15 Section section
16 Costner role in The Untouchables
22 Most docile
23 Shoot craps
29 Lotion additive
30 Castle protector
31 Emulate Durer
32 "Vaya con —"
33 Black fly
34 Gymnast Kerri
35 Hindu mystic
37 Roman robe
38 Claim
39 Word on a towel
41 Greene of Bonanza
46 Private Benjamin portrayer
47 "Pardon me"
49 Labor
50 Sabrina of TV
51 LAX info
52 Dogcatcher's find
53 Guide for the Wabash Cannonball
54 Wartime menace

**55** Latin step
**56** Job for Perry Mason
**57** Chopped
**58** Frost
**61** Adriatic wind
**62** Items at the PO
**63** Algerian officials
**65** Zoom or telephoto
**66** *Planet of the —*
**67** Forelimb bones
**69** Type of oil
**70** Obedience school master
**71** "Goody gumdrops!"

**72** Made fun of
**78** Confuse
**79** Stars and stripes, with "old"
**80** Suppress
**81** Dick and Jane's pet
**82** Israeli folk dance
**83** *— Called Horse*
**84** Mayberry character
**85** "Scat!"
**86** Pop of "Top of the Pops"
**87** Soothsayer
**88** Piccadilly Circus statue
**91** Boob tubes

# Puzzle 2-18: Undercover Work

### Across

1 Marble
6 In the lead
11 Newscaster Roger
15 Petri —
19 More laugh-provoking, in a way:var.
20 Grub, e.g.
21 Western American Indian
22 Water color
23 Schoolyard game
25 *Twister* star
27 View from the QE II
28 Supreme Diana
30 Translucent, as a gem
31 Masters and Johnson subject
32 "To Autumn" poet
34 A.k.a. the soul of wit
35 Microphone: abbr.
38 Dangerous driver

41 Teacher's grp.
42 *Angela's* — (Frank McCourt best-seller)
45 Has a go
46 Takes a position
48 Greenspan's domain, with "the"
51 Passive
52 Make a salad
53 Playful mammal
54 Take-charge person
55 Multiplex offering
56 "— Got Rhythm"
57 Guitar divisions
58 Vintner Ernest or Julio
59 Streisand title role
61 Tyrolean tune
62 Luxury furs
63 Eyebrow shape
65 Micronutrients
69 "— bodkins!"

70 Mackerel relations
72 Name in auto racing
73 Macaroni shape
75 Astrologer Sydney
76 Majority leader Dick
77 Model of honesty
79 Torch's work
82 X, sometimes
83 Lets loose
84 Gawked at
85 Bandage material
86 Suffix with legal or computer
87 Borscht basis
88 Bugged, in a quiet way
89 *Ghostbusters* goop
90 Socks, to Chelsea Clinton
91 He knew "What evil lurks . . ."
94 Feathers' adhesive
95 Rap group The — Boys
98 Noah or Wallace of screen
99 Button on the TV
102 "Tired of Being Alone" singer
103 Cain's victim
104 Polish coal-mining region
108 Ed Dodd comic strip
110 Résumé, perhaps
113 Free association result
114 Slaughter in baseball
115 "Ready or not, — come!"
116 One at — (singly)
117 Trawling needs
118 Art — (Thirties style)
119 Ford lemon
120 1999 Hall of Famer Ryan

## Down

1 Dr. Seuss' *Horton Hears* —
2 Camera man
3 Gofer
4 Babysitting Club members
5 Wipe out
6 *Same Time, Next Year* star
7 "My dog — fleas"
8 Poetic preposition
9 Finds the middle number
10 North and South states since 1889
11 Talc-to-diamond scale
12 Southwestern native
13 Sorrow
14 Dredge, for one
15 Pompom-shaped bloom
16 Towel-tosser's phrase
17 Optimistic
18 Misanthropic feeling
24 Bakery call

26 Church areas
29 Quick way to the UK
32 Russian ballet company
33 Beethoven dedicatee
34 Like old bones
35 Disfigure
36 — more (gone)
37 One of *The Three Amigos*
39 Head Hun
40 High regard
43 Cleveland's lake
44 Powerful speaker
47 Singer O'Connor
48 Copy an example
49 Caught congers
50 Metalworker's waste
53 "Pizza with the works," e.g.
54 Mousse measure
57 Speaker before Gingrich
58 Loudmouths
60 —-80 (early computer)
61 Assents
62 Monogram for McGwire
63 Heard the alarm
64 *Ghostbusters* actor Harold
66 Surgeon's tool
67 Intertwine
68 Must
71 Hosp. rooms
74 Like most antibiotics
76 YOU — HERE (map notation)
77 Annually, after "once"
78 Like a squinting gaze
80 L. Frank Baum princess
81 —-do-well
83 In shackles
84 King of England in A.D. 1000
87 Trouble
88 Fuming, Shakespeare style
90 Inuits' garb
92 Subside
93 Propelling sound
95 Switch attachment
96 Everglades wader
97 Cockamamie
100 City in SW New York
101 Right-hand page
102 "I — a pickle"
103 To boot
104 Big name in power tools
105 Nursery need
106 Cookbook author Rombauer
107 Gulf of —
109 Summer Games org.
111 Start of MGM's motto
112 Radio-size battery

# Puzzle 2-19: At the Beanery

## Across

1 French pastries
6 Comic strip Viking
11 Singer Mama —
15 Spun item
19 Tickle pink
20 Worship
21 Jai —
22 Spanish "she"
23 Gym bean?
25 Artistic beans?
27 Lupin of mysteries
28 Perform dreadfully
30 Take a new policy for
31 "A friend in — . . ."
33 Nobelist Bohr
35 "Resume speed," musically
36 Bit of baloney?
39 Country-style bean?
42 Neither follower
43 Cross to bear
45 Long tale
46 Spaghetti —
49 San Francisco sight
53 Lawn products brand name
55 Intro to physics?
57 "So help me"
60 Inflatable item, perhaps
61 Baggage handler
62 — und Drang
64 Indirect references
66 Nail salon's board
67 Bond bundle
69 Baseball player Galarraga
70 Suffix meaning "skin"
71 Anne's book about beans?
75 Old-time actor Tamiroff
78 Character actor J. — Naish
80 Cash register
81 Dictator's helper
82 Trattoria special
85 G and F, for two
88 Name tag word
89 Alley —
90 Haymaking chore
92 Spanish painter José Maria
93 Up and about
94 Kellogg competitor
96 Palmists, e.g.
98 Look like Tom?
100 Muscle or dial
101 FedEx predecessor
104 Leading beans?
107 Writer Buntline
108 Prairie dog's cousin
111 "— me" (big spender's phrase)
112 Dead Sea kingdom
114 Stimuli reactions
116 Furrows in a column
119 Came home
123 Offshore bean?
125 Grinder's bean?
127 Dill
128 Charges
129 Diminish
130 Beethoven dedicatee
131 Speak smart to
132 Three-piece, e.g.
133 Improve the roadway
134 Domingo, e.g.

## Down

1 Mexicali locale
2 Chinese border river
3 Hobos
4 Quaking tree
5 Anglers' nets
6 Old witch
7 Modifying wds.
8 Billy —
9 Following a circular path
10 Repairs a sweater
11 Cornfield cry
12 Controversial orchard sprays
13 —-Coburg-Gotha
14 Like an ape
15 Pudding
16 Alimentary canal segment
17 Soup eating sound
18 Small role
24 —-foot oil: var.
26 Biblical preposition
29 Rolling Stone Richards
32 Apothecary's weights
34 Author Jones (a.k.a. Imamu Amiri Baraka)
36 Settled, as the bill
37 "When —, do as . . ."
38 Bouquet of beans?
40 "And this is the thanks —?"
41 Mother of note
44 Union general
47 Chronicle of the year
48 Pasta order

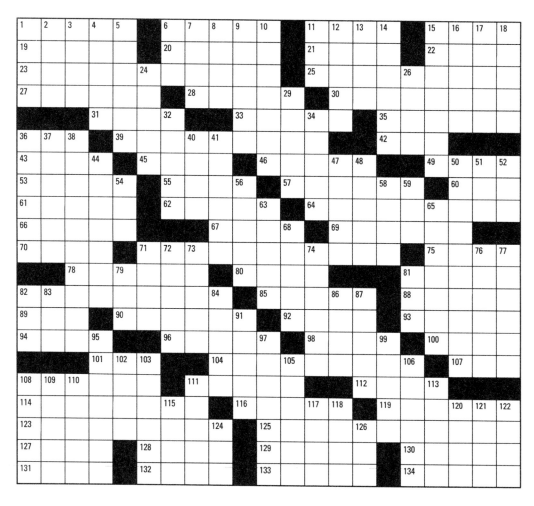

**50** Funny bean?
**51** Of yore
**52** Jan., Feb., etc.
**54** Adjectival suffix
**56** Ain't correct?
**58** Brewski
**59** Three times, in prescription code
**63** Copperfield's field
**65** Most shipshape
**68** Shopping havens
**71** Yago Sant'— (wine maker)
**72** Upscale auto
**73** *Dallas* matriarch
**74** Censors on live TV
**76** Kind of skates
**77** At anchor
**79** Letters on a color wheel
**81** — Na Na
**82** Soak up
**83** Whisper sweet nothings
**84** All thumbs
**86** Bite nails

**87** Blow off some —
**91** "Gag me!"
**95** Upheavals
**97** Hobbyist's racer
**99** Written language
**102** Nosegay
**103** Symbols of authority
**105** Dress for court
**106** Drawer deodorizer
**108** Goya subjects
**109** Where lions and gladiators meet
**110** Parts
**111** 1940s internees
**113** Calculus developer George
**115** Stead
**117** "— first you don't . . ."
**118** Aftershave maker
**120** Make a shambles of
**121** Petrol maker
**122** Caribou kin
**124** FDR's successor
**126** Suffix with rocket or racket

# *Puzzle 2-20: Location, Location, Location!*

The theme for this puzzle gives you the letters within the entry, but you must determine their location in the answer word.

## *Across*

1 Prado city
7 Grow up
13 Thickets
19 Idle
20 Popular wake-up time
21 The East
22 E-R-I
24 Maple leaf nation
25 Grazing spot
26 Eur. alliance
27 "— song of sixpence . . ."
29 So to speak, with "were"
30 Islet
31 Letter from Greece

32 Like some twentieth-century music
34 Garlic unit
35 "I — kick from champagne . . ."
37 M-E
41 Sparks from Hollywood
42 Part of the iris
44 Part of QED
45 Pucci of fashion
47 Gel
49 Musical opening
52 Ramps
55 Rotating shaft piece
58 L-E-S
60 Where Plato taught
61 Forget
63 Clay, today

**64** — *Fables*
**66** Punjab princess
**67** Pedro's mom
**69** Ninth-century emperor
**71** Stepped (upon)
**72** Reverses the dele
**73** "But the — not yet" (Matthew)
**74** Make the scene
**76** Links prop
**78** "— go bragh"
**79** Map collections
**81** H-E
**84** —-Kone (summer treat)
**85** Pete of The Weavers
**86** East or West ender
**87** Pilot
**89** Official population count
**92** Deserve
**94** Papal vestments
**98** Tandem Application Language
**100** T-A-G
**104** Avoid notice
**105** Egg-shaped
**107** Make up
**108** Like a beet
**110** Spat
**111** Slushy ice
**112** Prepared Granny Smith
**113** Getting — years
**115** Rest lead-in
**116** Melon
**118** A-I-R
**123** *Lend Me* — (Broadway show)
**124** Margarine ingredient
**125** "Who can I — . . ." (1941 hit song)
**126** Bar, at the bar
**127** Assemblies
**128** Was a ham

## Down

**1** Indian shoe, for short
**2** Studio
**3** Breakfast nook, perhaps
**4** Composer Nino
**5** Neighbor of Leb.
**6** Campus VIPs
**7** Reminder
**8** Fifth, for one
**9** Dutch painter — Borch
**10** As one, after "in"
**11** Kind of stripe
**12** Emerge
**13** Caesar's partner
**14** — *pro nobis*
**15** San Carlos Apache
**16** S-E-A-S
**17** Salad item
**18** Made known

**20** Fri. follower
**23** Not of the cloth
**28** Candlelight
**30** Sub-Zero counterpoint
**31** Word with opposite
**32** Simile center
**33** Iota
**34** Salt and wine containers
**36** Japanese drama
**38** Less trusting
**39** Measure, in Trieste
**40** File heading, for short
**43** Region
**46** Antiseptic salt
**48** Cowboys' home
**50** Took five
**51** Hebrew lyre
**53** Medical alkaloid: var.
**54** Is cornered, with "way out"
**55** —-you-are party
**56** More than *amie*
**57** A-S-S
**59** Bandleader Cugat
**60** "— to me . . . as ruddy drops"
   (Shakespeare)
**62** Allocation of medical resources
**65** Type of soil
**68** Vanilla, for one
**70** "What's Hecuba to him — to
   Hecuba?" (Hamlet)
**75** Diva Carol
**77** Columnist Bombeck
**80** Gaelic
**82** Mrs. Roosevelt
**83** Domesticated
**88** Zilch
**90** Ruin
**91** Sound systems
**93** Had a bite
**95** Grape's kin
**96** Descendant of Esau
**97** Stitch
**98** Puccini opera
**99** Copy 87 Across
**101** Proportional
**102** Obsessed (by)
**103** Part of HOMES
**106** U of the UN
**109** Related through Mom
**112** Complain
**113** Cornelia — Skinner
**114** Ice rink org.
**115** *Hair* hair
**117** Greeting for a villain
**119** Tick-tack-toe score
**120** Foot or paw: Danish
**121** "Fee, fie, foe, —, I smell . . ."
**122** Actor Steiger

# Part III
## Other Puzzle Fun

The 5th Wave · By Rich Tennant

In his later years, Captain Hook gave up on chasing Peter Pan and took up crossword puzzles.

## Puzzle 3-1

Every S in the puzzle stands for an I in the answer.

SF  SU  TEF  MEEB  OCTTNPU  FE  CBB
__  __  ___  ____  _____  __  ___

IPNCO  CTB  UAMCP  FE  VEAP  IEHHNN
_____  ___  _____  __  ____  _____

CHFNP  VEA  RCWN  ZEAPNB  SF  STFE
_____  ___  ____  _____  __  ____

VEAP  UCAINP.
____  _____.

## Puzzle 3-2

Every M in the puzzle stands for a D in the answer.

MFM  THK  WVLI  LUHKC  CWV  MKDX  JWH
___  ___  ____  _____  ___  ____  ___

JVYC  CH  CWV  MIKNRCHIV  CH  UKT
____  __  ___  _____  __  ___

RHPV  DWLQRCFDX  LYM  LRXVM  CWV
____  _____  ___  _____  ___

QWLIPLDRFC  CH  QKC  FC  HY  WFR
_____  __  ___  __  __  ___

UFGG?
____?

# Puzzle 3-3

Every V in the puzzle stands for an H in the answer.

QVK ALCIQ QVDGP XWLHQ GKA WLLFI
___ _____ _____ _____ ___ _____

DI QVXQ QVKB FKKU HI OCLJ
__ ____ ____ ____ __ ____

CKXZDGP QVK LYZ LGKI. (ELIKUV
_____ ___ ___ ____. (_____

ELHWKCQ)
_____)

# Puzzle 3-4

Every A in the puzzle stands for a B in the answer.

AN IKK DVIRY DISSN. CH NXM JVU
__ ___ _____ _____. __ ___ ___

I JXXP DIUV NXM TCKK AV OILLN;
_ ____ ____ ___ ____ __ _____;

IRP CH NXM JVU I AIP XRV NXM
___ __ ___ ___ _ ___ ___ ___

TCKK AVBXDV I LOCKXYXLOVS.
____ _____ _ _____.

## Puzzle 3-5

HINT

Every N in the puzzle stands for an A in the answer.

```
ENZZDFX  LOJJ  ZDWDF  TD  HQJJB
_____  ____  _____  __  _____

PTXDFWDC  QZAOJ  XPEDPZD  OZWDZAX
_____  _____  _____  _____

XDJH-LOZCOZY  XVNYMDAAO  NZC
____-_____  _____  ___

OZWOXOTJD  APPAMVOIUX.
_____  _____.
```

## Puzzle 3-6

HINT

Every J in the puzzle stands for an I in the answer.

```
JB  TX  BJEZX  DAQ  WAI'X  ZQSSOOW,
__  __  _____  ___  ___'_  _____,

XED  TPTJI.  XMOI  CQJX:  IA  QZO
___  _____.  ____  ____:  __  ___

GOJIP  T  WTEI  BAAK  TGAQX  JX.
_____  _  ____  ____  _____  __.

(R.  S.  BJOKWZ)
(_.  _.  _____)
```

# Puzzle 3-7: 21 x 15 Squares

1 Across begins in the second box from the left in the top row.

## Across

1 California trial judge Lance
4 *Dianetics* author — Hubbard
5 Word of acceptance
8 River through Aragon
12 Professional lives
16 Bone dry
18 "Mack the Knife" singer
19 Room for study
20 Spring bulb
23 Motion studies
25 Rub out
26 Backpack
27 Beginning of Scrooge's remark
30 K-O bridge
31 1991 US Open champ
32 Bathing suit maker
35 Blue jeans go-with
39 *Cheers* setting
42 In full flower
43 *2001* computer
44 Pledge against loss
47 NYC opera house, after "The"
48 Follow the — (schoolyard game)

51 Despot
52 Jane's hubby
53 "— little teapot . . ."
55 Old Ford model
56 Elected law-making body
61 Rose feature
64 Volume boosters
66 Pigs
67 Org. for 31 Across
70 Happening
71 Choir member
72 Mystic teachings
74 Hawaiian goose
75 Downcast
76 Cholesterol-rich food
77 CBS logo

## Down

1 Dies —
2 Shredded
3 Word before "blast off"
4 Calculator display
5 Chatter on
6 Actor Estrada
7 Wrongdoer
8 "I could — horse!"
9 —-a-brac

10 Humphrey's *Casablanca* role
11 Switch positions
13 Summer in France
14 Capek play
15 Ski course
17 Gave out the cards
18 — *Boot*
21 Belief
22 Shut in
24 Westminster workers: abbr.
27 Baden-Powell's org.
28 EMT SOS
29 Steering gear
33 Want ad letters
34 Polka —
36 — Na Na
37 At the end of one's rope, with "it"
38 — de la Cite
39 Purchase
40 Airport posting
41 — estate
44 Inert
45 Cable channel
46 CPA's column
48 First name in TV talk
49 Detroit duds
50 Tears
52 Prefix with cycle
54 Kitty's cry
56 Spelunker's place
57 Farm animals
58 Stitch in time saver
59 Zero degrees longitude
60 Ms, in Madrid
62 Santa —, CA
63 Neighbor of Syr.
64 Door sign
65 Turf
67 Strategem
68 Strong storm
69 Question
73 Sailor's reply

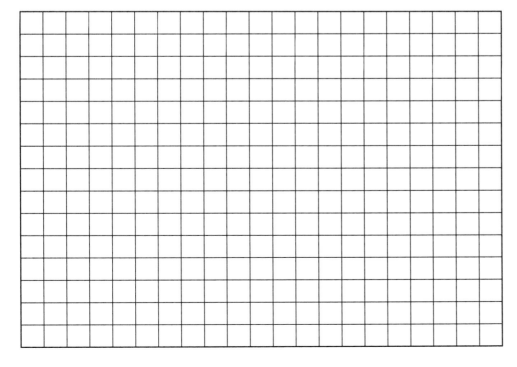

# Puzzle 3-8: 23 x 15 Squares

1 Across begins in the fourth square from the left in the top row.

## Across

1 Kitchen wrap brand
5 — *of Eden*
9 Astounded
10 Disrobe
12 Baby frog
14 Short stay
17 NBC rival
18 Dream session
21 Opposite NNW
24 Seine sight
25 Meadowland
26 Lyric poem
28 Come to pass
31 Once named
32 Place for Trix
35 Enclosed
38 Andrea — (ill-fated ship)
39 Perfect, NASA style
41 Catchall abbr.
42 Speak publicly
43 Neptune's domain
44 Mass calendar
45 Avia rival
47 Lawyer's exam
48 Scandinavian

50 Blue element
53 Nourish
54 Kidnap
55 Alternate musical passage
56 Do a teacher's job
57 — apso (small dog)
61 Connect to the Internet
62 Actor Gig
63 Dowel

## Down

1 Mkt. value
2 Indochinese language
3 Shoemaker's tool
4 Actress Ruby
5 Dangerous curve
6 Phone co.
7 Full house sign
8 Knock over
9 Passports or licenses
11 Hunting hound
12 Body powder
13 Busy as —
15 Skedaddle
16 Nourish

18 Pooh's friend
19 Christopher Marlowe drama
20 In tune
21 Railroad workers
22 Fast food purveyor
23 Wordless communication
26 Actor Wallach
27 Law enforcement org.
29 Bob Hope's org.
30 EMU setting
33 Employment letters
34 Coach Parseghian
36 Pet dog
37 Take it one day — time
40 *People's Court* judge Ed
41 Env. Fillers
44 Hockey legend's family
46 "I could — horse!"
48 Classic beginning
49 Switch position
51 Calculator screen
52 Tea for deux
58 Hula —
59 Chills
60 Top 40 nominee

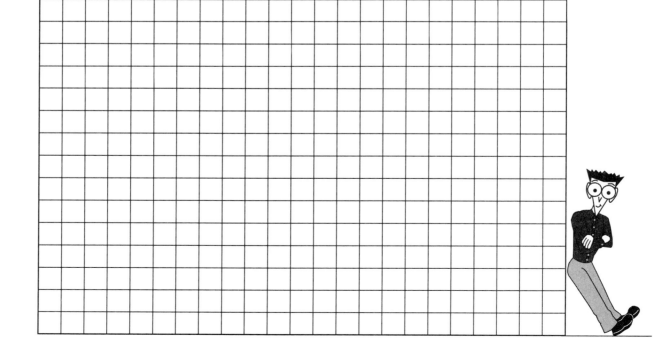

# Puzzle 3-9: 17 x 19 Squares

1 Across begins in the first square at the top left corner.

## Across

1 Hawaiian garland
4 TV network
7 "To — is human . . ."
8 Call for help
11 *The Parent —*
12 Title for Edna Everage
14 Actor Penn
15 Miss Keeler
16 Lariat
19 Fuel
21 Drop down
23 Old-time airline
24 It may end with .com
25 Stick (to)
29 Entertainment co.
31 Place for a splint
35 Cereal container
36 Advanced degrees
38 Singular
39 Loathe
40 Carriage
41 Explosive initials
42 Ice-cream holder
43 Produce an egg
44 Four, on the phone
45 Before Carson and Leno
47 Overweight
50 El — (Rio Grande city)
52 Like a kite
53 Lupino of Hollywood
54 Nick and Nora's pet
55 City bus driver's org.
56 Remove from a text
58 Disapproving sound
59 Edible bivalve
63 — Baba
65 On the peak
67 Card player's phrase
69 Old gold coin of Spain
72 Goatee
75 Settled a bill
76 *Return of the Jedi* creature
77 Slim down
79 Otherwise
80 Sitcom alien
81 Baseball —
82 Diamond, e.g.
83 Lodge brother

## Down

1 Took by the hand
2 Of time

3 — *La Douce*
4 Nestle's treat
5 Movie pig
6 Undercover agent
8 Red or Dead
9 Int'l group since '48
10 Stuck-up person
11 Group of three
13 Hazardous road curve
14 NCO
17 Patrol vehicle
18 Joint pronoun
20 Mauna —
22 Jolson and Capp
26 Israeli statesman Abba
27 Learning by repetition
28 English river
29 Speed limit letters
30 Braided egg bread
32 Sweltering
33 Roadside lodge
34 After taxes
37 The limit, of saying
39 Lifts

42 Discipline
44 Student's ranking, for short
45 "What a —!" (Too bad)
46 Turkish bigwigs
47 Repair
48 Fuss
49 Sigma follower
51 Grown-up acorn
52 Health service grp.
57 Rap lightly
60 Chinese philosophy
61 Practice piece
62 Hold up
64 Scientist's workroom
66 Beg
67 Writing liquid
68 Unhappy
69 Valley
70 Night bird
71 Deflating sound
73 Pudding or paddy
74 "It's a —!"
75 Wooden pin
78 Toll rd.

# Puzzle 3-10: 23 x 15 Squares

**HINT**

1 Across begins in the ninth square from the left in the top row.

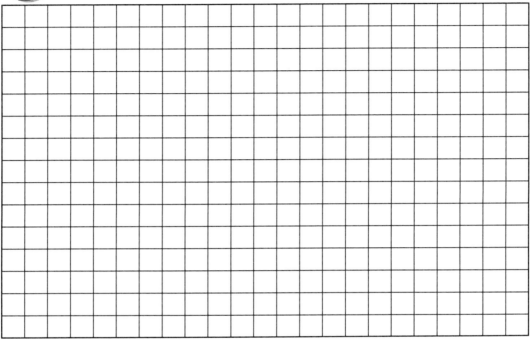

## Across

1 Arnold Palmer's org.
4 Raw material
7 Blots out
12 Defiant to authority
14 Polite refusal
16 Chairman —
17 Type of numeral
20 Output from 6 Down
21 Tell all
23 Singer Frankie
25 Andes climber
28 Take — (conquer)
31 Dragged along
33 Observe
34 Carbonated beverage
36 Disturb the peace
37 — *Boot* (German film)
38 Nearby
40 "Messiah" composer
42 Lamb's lament
43 White-tailed bird
45 Perfect score
46 24 hours
47 Rocky abbr.
48 Kiddy card game
49 Actor Carney
50 Designer label
51 Not friend
52 Beret's relation

54 Temp. teacher
55 Wide shoe size
57 Split — soup
59 Western native
61 Large tank
64 *Exodus* hero
65 Crew
66 Common connection
67 Animation collectible
68 Paul Bunyan's tool
69 Lottery pix

## Down

1 "And pulled out a —" (Jack Horner)
2 Supporting piece
3 Molecule
4 Church calendar
5 Heyerdahl craft
6 Sicilian erupter
7 "— Clear Day. . ."
8 Baden-Powell's org.
9 Failed amendment
10 Keep one's — to the ground
11 Depot, for short
12 "— Yankee Doodle Dandy . . ."
13 Recede, as the tide
14 Prefix for second
15 Exaggerate

18 Uncomfortable
19 Colombian city
20 Picture publication
22 Hairless
23 Wt.
24 Seafaring word
26 — culpa
27 Mag. revenue
29 "You're a Grand Old Flag" penner
30 Writer LeShan
31 Can, UK style
32 Actor MacDowell
35 From the top
36 Carry on
38 Munitions
39 Mild expletive
40 Alpert of music
41 Singer — Lovett
44 DC lobby
45 Frat letter
51 Flunk
53 NYC landmark
54 Measure of volume
56 Novelist Hunter
57 —-man (video game)
58 "Able was I — . . ."
60 Assessment
62 A year in Castille
63 NFL scores

# Puzzle 3-11: 19 x 19 Squares

1 Across begins in the seventh square from the left top corner.

## Across

1 Pollution watchdog grp.
4 Water barrier
7 DC official
8 "— body meets a body . . ."
9 Type of strap
12 Pucker
14 PA reactor site
16 Tacit assent
17 Stitch up
18 Loathing
20 Dangerous snake
21 Scramble up
24 Gaiters
26 South Seas barbecue
27 Just getting by, with "out"
30 Belief
31 Roman god of war
32 Fool
33 Iron
34 The — and the Papas
35 Ambulance team member: abbr.
36 Type size
37 Owns
40 Mister, Mexican style
41 Young haddock
46 Square measure
48 From a distance
49 "— were the days, my friend . . ."
50 Smart aleck, after "know"
52 Storklike bird
53 Dilapidated
54 Blockbuster movie of '98
56 Letters on a letter
57 Ferber of fiction
58 More than once, poetically
61 Dustcloth
62 Start of the wk.
63 Offensive
65 Popular pencil game
68 Type of truck
69 TV frequency
70 "— hoo!"
71 Caspian, e.g.

## Down

1 Sports network
2 Reaches the top
3 Point of view
4 A cube
5 Nautical position
6 Grumpy old man Walter
9 Comic Caesar
10 Chop
11 Moslem holy man
12 $100 bills
13 Swelters
15 The Beatles' "Let —"
19 Sounds when you see a mouse
20 Downfall
21 Museum type
22 Woody Allen ex Louise
23 Pilaf ingredient
24 Engine additive
25 — annum
26 Thin outer covering
28 *Platoon* setting
29 Zero degrees longitude
31 Evil
34 Iron-rich range
37 "Bali —" (*South Pacific* song)
38 Paintings
39 Usher
41 "Down by the old Mill — . . ."
42 Revise
43 Coll. Military course
44 East, in Essen
45 Susan of *L.A. Law*
47 "I cannot tell —" (George Washington)
51 Old Ford models
52 Foolishness
55 "Are you some kind of —?"
58 Two-match connection
59 Zero in on
60 A tenth part
61 Caviar
64 Couch
66 Dove call
67 Pair

# *Puzzle 3-12: Embracing Shadows*

**A** Sitcom featuring the Bunker family (3, 2, 3, 6)

$\overline{101}\ \overline{141}\ \overline{177}\ \overline{85}\ \overline{22}\ \overline{166}\ \overline{38}\ \overline{41}\ \overline{113}\ \overline{49}$
$\overline{169}\ \overline{96}\ \overline{7}\ \overline{117}$

**B** English muffin features (5, 3, 8)

$\overline{84}\ \overline{168}\ \overline{2}\ \overline{74}\ \overline{30}\ \overline{156}\ \overline{64}\ \overline{95}\ \overline{50}\ \overline{19}$
$\overline{36}\ \overline{143}\ \overline{52}\ \overline{174}\ \overline{79}\ \overline{127}$

**C** Ruining the appearance of

$\overline{153}\ \overline{83}\ \overline{172}\ \overline{110}\ \overline{104}\ \overline{144}\ \overline{134}\ \overline{68}\ \overline{18}\ \overline{99}$
$\overline{27}$

**D** Producing the desired result; taking place

$\overline{26}\ \overline{175}\ \overline{82}\ \overline{100}\ \overline{102}\ \overline{37}\ \overline{160}\ \overline{78}\ \overline{10}$

**E** Vexed; decorated with pleats

$\overline{121}\ \overline{119}\ \overline{116}\ \overline{152}\ \overline{76}\ \overline{126}\ \overline{15}$

**F** Space transportation

$\overline{155}\ \overline{93}\ \overline{128}\ \overline{89}\ \overline{24}\ \overline{48}\ \overline{170}$

**G** Win an endurance test

$\overline{58}\ \overline{61}\ \overline{66}\ \overline{111}\ \overline{131}\ \overline{91}\ \overline{70}$

**H** Snack chip

$\overline{165}\ \overline{73}\ \overline{103}\ \overline{145}\ \overline{109}$

**I** "Hold on"

$\overline{173}\ \overline{46}\ \overline{112}\ \overline{56}$

**J** Tiny (4-5)

$\overline{98}\ \overline{17}\ \overline{108}\ \overline{178}\ \overline{32}\ \overline{53}\ \overline{162}\ \overline{39}\ \overline{69}$

**K** "One — under God . . ."

$\overline{161}\ \overline{149}\ \overline{67}\ \overline{88}\ \overline{65}\ \overline{34}$

**L** Tax crime

$\overline{75}\ \overline{97}\ \overline{11}\ \overline{6}\ \overline{115}\ \overline{151}\ \overline{107}$

**M** Try for a basket

$\overline{43}\ \overline{25}\ \overline{71}\ \overline{77}\ \overline{123}$

**N** Life stories: abbr.

$\overline{125}\ \overline{21}\ \overline{44}\ \overline{62}$

**O** State; thorough

$\overline{59}\ \overline{138}\ \overline{137}\ \overline{87}\ \overline{28}$

**P** Deeply engrossing

$\overline{129}\ \overline{13}\ \overline{3}\ \overline{140}\ \overline{120}\ \overline{154}\ \overline{45}\ \overline{23}$

**Q** Ate quickly

$\overline{54}\ \overline{159}\ \overline{132}\ \overline{47}\ \overline{1}\ \overline{42}\ \overline{80}$

**R** Wearing rose-colored glasses

$\overline{124}\ \overline{157}\ \overline{135}\ \overline{90}\ \overline{72}\ \overline{5}\ \overline{16}\ \overline{147}\ \overline{8}\ \overline{167}$

**S** Sampler motto (4, 5, 4)

$\overline{139}\ \overline{146}\ \overline{163}\ \overline{81}\ \overline{31}\ \overline{12}\ \overline{35}\ \overline{4}\ \overline{92}\ \overline{55}$
$\overline{142}\ \overline{60}\ \overline{130}$

**T** One with a stake in the action (10, 5)

$\overline{136}\ \overline{14}\ \overline{86}\ \overline{106}\ \overline{20}\ \overline{94}\ \overline{171}\ \overline{176}\ \overline{114}\ \overline{148}$
$\overline{158}\ \overline{29}\ \overline{40}\ \overline{63}\ \overline{122}$

**U** *Fargo* assent (4-5)

$\overline{118}\ \overline{51}\ \overline{164}\ \overline{150}\ \overline{105}\ \overline{133}\ \overline{9}\ \overline{33}\ \overline{57}$

| 1O | 2B | 3P | 4S | | 5R | 6L | | 7A | 8R | 9U | 10D | | 11L | | 12S | 13P | 14T | 15E | | 16R | 17J | 18C | 19B | 20T | 21N | 22A | 23P |
|---|---|---|---|---|---|---|---|---|---|---|---|---|---|---|---|---|---|---|---|---|---|---|---|---|---|---|---|
| | 24F | 25M | 26D | | 27C | 28O | 29T | 30B | 31S | | 32J | 33U | 34K | 35S | 36B | 37D | 38A | | 39J | 40T | 41A | 42Q | 43M | | 44N | 45P | |
| 46I | | 47O | 48F | 49A | 50B | 51U | | 52B | 53J | 54Q | 55S | 56I | | 57U | 58G | 59O | | 60S | 61G | 62N | 63T | | 64B | 65K | 66G | | 67K |
| 68C | 69J | | 70G | 71M | | 72R | 73H | 74B | 75L | | 76E | 77M | 78D | 79B | | 80Q | 81S | 82D | 83C | 84B | 85A | 86T | 87O | | | 88K | 89F |
| | 90R | 91G | | 92S | 93F | 94T | | 95B | 96A | 97L | 98J | 99C | 100D | | 101A | 102D | 103H | 104C | 105U | 106T | 107L | 108J | | 109H | 110C | | 111G |
| 112I | 113A | 114T | | 115L | 116E | | 117A | 118U | 119E | | 120P | 121E | 122T | | 123M | 124R | | 125N | 126E | | 127B | 128F | 129P | 130S | | 131G |
| 132Q | 133U | 134C | 135R | | 136T | 137O | | 138O | 139S | 140P | | 141A | 142S | 143B | 144C | | 145H | 146S | 147R | | 148T | 149K | 150U | | 151L | 152E |
| 153C | 154P | 155F | 156B | 157R | 158T | 159Q | 160D | 161K | 162J | 163S | 164U | 165H | 166A | | 167R | 168B | 169A | 170F | 171T | | 172C | 173I | 174B | 175D | 176T | 177A | 178J |

# Puzzle 3-13: Tip of the Iceberg

**A** On one's uppers (4, 3, 3)

___ ___ ___ ___ ___ ___ ___ ___ ___ ___
125 48 16 107 66 89 38 94 127 44

**B** British form of football

___ ___ ___ ___ ___
18 67 32 112 81

**C** Key meringue ingredients (3, 6)

___ ___ ___ ___ ___ ___ ___ ___ ___
23 101 95 40 1 111 62 72 133

**D** Rude; fresh

___ ___ ___ ___ ___ ___ ___ ___
119 56 126 17 60 8 78 114

**E** Betray; use up the inventory (4, 3)

___ ___ ___ ___ ___ ___ ___
122 116 49 73 39 33 4

**F** Bugs Bunny's nemesis (5, 4)

___ ___ ___ ___ ___ ___ ___ ___ ___
96 64 51 57 5 115 109 68 19

**G** Critic's job

___ ___ ___ ___ ___ ___ ___ ___ ___
22 55 47 74 80 3 10 59 92

**H** Five o'clock shadow

___ ___ ___ ___ ___ ___ ___
131 15 50 24 70 113 34

**I** Phrase of frustration (3, 3, 2)

___ ___ ___ ___ ___ ___ ___ ___
61 30 46 36 82 110 88 97

**J** Daytime TV fare

___ ___ ___ ___
77 2 123 129

**K** Melts

___ ___ ___ ___ ___
27 13 87 54 41

**L** Enjoys a TV dinner (4, 2)

___ ___ ___ ___ ___ ___
99 58 63 11 90 75

**M** Religious ceremony

___ ___ ___ ___
128 106 9 117

**N** Fast cat

___ ___ ___ ___ ___ ___ ___
85 98 84 52 12 37 28

**O** Easily sprained joints

___ ___ ___ ___ ___ ___
104 120 76 71 65 53

**P** Traffic jam time of day (4, 4)

___ ___ ___ ___ ___ ___ ___ ___
83 6 20 45 79 42 25 102

**Q** Type of agent (4, 6)

___ ___ ___ ___ ___ ___ ___ ___ ___ ___
100 7 14 118 132 35 105 108 26 29

**R** Completely distracted (2, 1, 3)

___ ___ ___ ___ ___ ___
69 91 21 43 130 121

**S** Allen of the Green Mountain Boys

___ ___ ___ ___ ___
103 93 86 31 124

| 1C | 2J | 3G | | 4E | 5F | 6P | 7Q | | 8D | 9M | | 10G | 11L | | 12N |
|---|---|---|---|---|---|---|---|---|---|---|---|---|---|---|---|
| 13K | 14Q | 15H | | 16A | 17D | 18B | 19F | 20P | | 21R | 22G | 23C | | 24H | 25P |
| 26Q | | 27K | 28N | 29Q | | 30I | 31S | 32B | 33E | 34H | | 35Q | 36I | 37N | 38A |
| 39E | 40C | 41K | | 42P | 43R | | 44A | 45P | 46I | | 47G | 48A | 49E | 50H | 51F |
| 52N | 53Q | | 54K | 55G | | 56D | 57F | 58L | 59Q | | 60D | 61I | 62C | 63L | 64F |
| 65O | | 66A | 67B | 68F | 69R | 70H | 71O | 72C | | 73E | 74G | 75L | 76O | 77J | |
| 78D | 79P | 80G | 81B | | 82I | 83P | 84N | | 85N | 86S | 87K | 88I | 89A | 90L | 91R |
| 92G | | 93S | 94A | 95C | 96F | 97I | 98N | 99L | 100Q | | 101C | 102P | 103S | 104O | 105Q |
| | 106M | 107A | 108Q | 109F | 110I | 111C | 112B | 113H | 114D | | 115F | 116E | 117M | 118Q | 119D |
| 120O | 121R | 122E | | 123J | 124S | 125A | | 126D | 127A | 128M | 129J | 130R | 131H | 132Q | 133C |

# Puzzle 3-14: A Wicked World

**A** Ungulate

‾14‾ ‾27‾ ‾90‾ ‾100‾ ‾60‾ ‾76‾

**B** Show submissive respect

‾143‾ ‾6‾ ‾62‾ ‾118‾ ‾127‾ ‾114‾

**C** Arm of the Atlantic connecting with the North Sea (7, 7)

‾9‾ ‾38‾ ‾47‾ ‾55‾ ‾101‾ ‾80‾ ‾105‾ ‾142‾ ‾20‾ ‾84‾
‾117‾ ‾135‾ ‾147‾ ‾125‾

**D** Political radical

‾13‾ ‾30‾ ‾40‾ ‾48‾ ‾56‾ ‾144‾ ‾89‾

**E** Treat for Dobbin (4, 2, 5)

‾33‾ ‾12‾ ‾17‾ ‾29‾ ‾67‾ ‾57‾ ‾138‾ ‾150‾ ‾96‾ ‾141‾
‾108‾

**F** Escarole

‾34‾ ‾46‾ ‾66‾ ‾107‾ ‾53‾ ‾24‾

**G** General survey; critical examination

‾140‾ ‾110‾ ‾123‾ ‾54‾ ‾37‾ ‾126‾

**H** Breaking the commandments

‾4‾ ‾1‾ ‾148‾ ‾102‾ ‾134‾ ‾88‾ ‾103‾

**I** Countryish; resembling a woolen fabric

‾2‾ ‾16‾ ‾116‾ ‾92‾ ‾121‾ ‾61‾

**J** Shirley Temple hit song, with Word Q (2, 3, 4, 4)

‾15‾ ‾68‾ ‾21‾ ‾43‾ ‾120‾ ‾25‾ ‾86‾ ‾113‾ ‾130‾ ‾35‾
‾49‾ ‾124‾ ‾73‾

**K** Give a new title to

‾10‾ ‾52‾ ‾149‾ ‾81‾ ‾115‾ ‾133‾

**L** The Abominable Snowman

‾70‾ ‾50‾ ‾77‾ ‾3‾

**M** Frequently

‾26‾ ‾11‾ ‾58‾ ‾74‾ ‾93‾

**N** Established; cast in metal

‾91‾ ‾99‾ ‾18‾ ‾7‾ ‾131‾ ‾79‾ ‾8‾

**O** Boxer Julio Cesar Green, for one

‾85‾ ‾22‾ ‾28‾ ‾39‾ ‾111‾ ‾83‾ ‾5‾ ‾71‾ ‾132‾ ‾42‾
‾119‾ ‾139‾

**P** Vigorous and buoyant

‾97‾ ‾145‾ ‾64‾ ‾104‾ ‾78‾ ‾109‾ ‾128‾ ‾98‾

**Q** See Word J

‾65‾ ‾63‾ ‾69‾ ‾129‾ ‾137‾ ‾32‾ ‾31‾ ‾36‾

**R** Commingle

‾41‾ ‾23‾ ‾82‾ ‾151‾ ‾72‾

**S** "There's no such thing as a —" (4, 5)

‾146‾ ‾95‾ ‾122‾ ‾94‾ ‾112‾ ‾87‾ ‾75‾ ‾19‾ ‾136‾

**T** *Ethan Frome* author Wharton

‾106‾ ‾51‾ ‾45‾ ‾44‾ ‾59‾

| | 1H | 2I | | 3L | 4H | | 5O | 6B | 7N | 8N | 9C | 10K | 11M | 12E | 13D | | 14A | 15J | 16I |
|---|---|---|---|---|---|---|---|---|---|---|---|---|---|---|---|---|---|---|---|
| | 17E | 18N | 19S | 20C | | 21J | 22O | 23R | 24F | | 25J | 26M | 27A | 28O | | 29E | 30D | 31Q | 32Q | 33E |
| 34F | | 35J | 36Q | 37G | 38C | 39O | | 40D | 41R | 42O | 43J | 44T | 45T | 46F | 47C | | 48D | 49J | 50L |
| 51T | 52K | 53F | 54G | 55C | | 56D | 57E | | 58M | 59T | 60A | 61I | | 62B | 63Q | 64P | 65Q | 66F | | 67E |
| 68J | 69Q | 70L | | 71O | 72R | 73J | 74M | 75S | 76A | | 77L | 78P | 79N | | 80C | 81K | 82R | 83O | | 84C |
| 85O | 86J | 87S | 88H | 89D | | 90A | 91N | | 92J | 93M | 94S | 95S | 96E | 97P | | 98P | 99N | 100A | 101C | 102H |
| 103H | | 104P | 105C | 106T | 107F | 108E | | 109P | 110G | 111O | 112S | 113J | 114B | | 115K | 116I | 117C | | 118B | 119O |
| 120J | | 121I | 122R | 123G | 124J | 125C | | 126G | 127B | 128P | 129Q | 130J | | 131N | 132O | 133K | | 134H | 135C |
| 136S | 137Q | 138E | | 139O | 140G | 141E | 142C | 143B | 144D | | 145P | 146S | | 147C | 148H | 149K | 150E | 151R | |

# Puzzle 3-15: Looks Are Deceiving

**A** Boxer Carlos Ortiz; featherbrain

‾102‾ ‾76‾ ‾139‾ ‾2‾ ‾36‾ ‾55‾ ‾42‾ ‾115‾ ‾9‾ ‾37‾ ‾106‾

**B** Southern pie specialty (4-3)

‾1‾ ‾137‾ ‾46‾ ‾62‾ ‾99‾ ‾96‾ ‾86‾

**C** Chord notation, in music

‾8‾ ‾39‾ ‾60‾ ‾174‾ ‾25‾ ‾168‾ ‾162‾ ‾73‾

**D** Noxious gases; seethes

‾64‾ ‾4‾ ‾124‾ ‾58‾ ‾18‾

**E** British actor Novello

‾140‾ ‾20‾ ‾112‾ ‾61‾

**F** Prognosticated

‾50‾ ‾35‾ ‾51‾ ‾80‾ ‾98‾ ‾43‾ ‾93‾

**G** Future promise (4, 4)

‾47‾ ‾6‾ ‾14‾ ‾72‾ ‾172‾ ‾31‾ ‾65‾ ‾85‾

**H** "— effect" (warming of the earth's surface)

‾33‾ ‾22‾ ‾13‾ ‾48‾ ‾77‾ ‾133‾ ‾97‾ ‾24‾ ‾5‾ ‾83‾

**I** Has a hankering

‾19‾ ‾27‾ ‾40‾ ‾121‾ ‾87‾ ‾7‾

**J** Former province of central France

‾56‾ ‾100‾ ‾141‾ ‾177‾ ‾30‾ ‾78‾ ‾116‾ ‾3‾

**K** Without question (2, 5)

‾17‾ ‾10‾ ‾54‾ ‾92‾ ‾130‾ ‾45‾ ‾57‾

**L** Lever that controls an electrical circuit (6, 6)

‾111‾ ‾91‾ ‾90‾ ‾148‾ ‾101‾ ‾161‾ ‾88‾ ‾132‾ ‾103‾ ‾179‾
‾108‾ ‾173‾

**M** Cowboy

‾29‾ ‾154‾ ‾68‾ ‾44‾ ‾66‾ ‾59‾ ‾53‾ ‾95‾

**N** Delicate air layer

‾23‾ ‾160‾ ‾52‾ ‾32‾ ‾118‾ ‾49‾ ‾15‾ ‾41‾ ‾134‾ ‾84‾ ‾21‾

**O** The Boston Pops, for one

‾34‾ ‾70‾ ‾94‾ ‾82‾ ‾16‾ ‾67‾ ‾81‾ ‾175‾ ‾89‾

**P** *Sabu* director Alexander

‾109‾ ‾28‾ ‾75‾ ‾12‾ ‾69‾

**Q** West Indies form of witchcraft

‾11‾ ‾74‾ ‾38‾ ‾71‾ ‾180‾

**R** Imposed upon

‾145‾ ‾63‾ ‾107‾ ‾105‾ ‾163‾ ‾26‾ ‾151‾

**S** Children; copy of a magazine

‾166‾ ‾136‾ ‾156‾ ‾119‾ ‾142‾

**T** Ancient Greek prescription for sorrow

‾135‾ ‾178‾ ‾104‾ ‾159‾ ‾157‾ ‾131‾ ‾128‾ ‾122‾

**U** Like a judge

‾169‾ ‾79‾ ‾129‾ ‾158‾ ‾114‾

**V** City in southeastern Turkey, formerly Edessa

‾171‾ ‾123‾ ‾146‾ ‾147‾

**W** Politician Henry Cabot —

‾152‾ ‾125‾ ‾155‾ ‾117‾ ‾138‾

**X** Overly (3-3)

‾127‾ ‾149‾ ‾153‾ ‾120‾ ‾170‾ ‾150‾

**Y** Implacable

‾143‾ ‾176‾ ‾126‾ ‾113‾ ‾164‾ ‾144‾ ‾165‾ ‾167‾

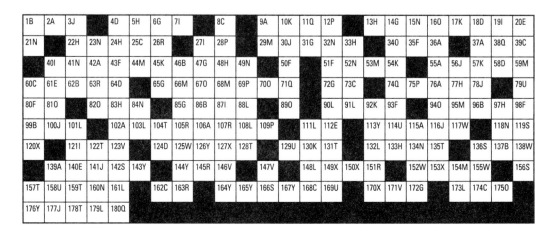

# Puzzle 3-16: What's In a Name?

**A** Before "ship out" (5, 2)

— — — — — — —
78 92 109 185 29 69 73

**B** Self-evident truth

— — — — —
95 30 111 83 67

**C** Bakery mold (6, 3)

— — — — — — — — —
154 132 100 116 200 49 33 125 151

**D** Kind of motive

— — — — — — — —
139 8 22 164 108 155 210 53

**E** Likeness

— — — — — —
52 56 118 216 124 72

**F** "Get a —!" (come look) (4, 2, 4)

— — — — — — — — — —
202 115 186 166 98 179 204 65 3 114

**G** Park seat

— — — — —
209 198 168 133 79

**H** Quite odd; out of character

— — — — — — —
48 82 181 217 150 7 220

**I** Before the Table of Contents (5, 4)

— — — — — — — — —
57 89 161 9 17 23 31 96 203

**J** Laid back (6, 6)

— — — — — — — — — —
71 147 143 63 85 123 4 55 194 206

— —
38 46

**K** School for Prince William

— — — —
34 149 1 165

**L** Lab monkey

— — — — — —
148 51 214 90 174 158

**M** Popeye's production company (7,7)

— — — — — — — — — —
88 176 27 208 199 138 107 91 58 221

— — — —
117 110 35 157

**N** Cover a loss, with "bet" (5, 4)

— — — — — — — — —
134 172 169 142 127 47 25 80 70

**O** Production; exertion

— — — — — —
191 192 32 180 18 218

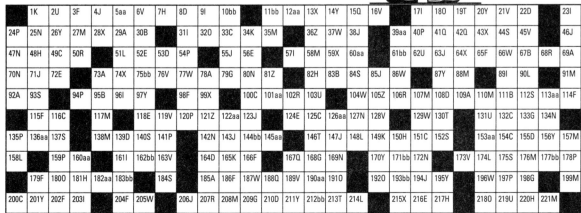

| | 1K | 2U | 3F | 4J | 5aa | 6V | 7H | 8D | 9I | 10bb | | 11bb | 12aa | 13X | 14Y | 15Q | 16V | | 17I | 18O | 19T | 20Y | 21V | 22D | | 23I |
|---|---|---|---|---|---|---|---|---|---|---|---|---|---|---|---|---|---|---|---|---|---|---|---|---|---|---|
| 24P | 25N | 26Y | 27M | 28X | 29A | 30B | | 31I | 32O | 33C | 34K | 35M | | 36Z | 37W | 38J | | 39aa | 40P | 41Q | 42Q | 43X | 44S | 45V | 46J |
| 47N | 48H | 49C | 50R | | 51L | 52E | 53D | 54P | | 55J | 56E | | 57I | 58M | 59X | 60aa | | 61bb | 62U | 63J | 64X | 65F | 66W | 67B | 68R | 69A |
| 70N | 71J | 72E | | 73A | 74X | 75bb | 76V | 77W | 78A | 79G | 80N | 81Z | | 82H | 83B | 84S | 85J | 86W | | 87Y | 88M | | 89I | 90L | | 91M |
| 92A | 93S | | 94P | 95B | 96I | 97Y | | 98F | 99X | | 100C | 101aa | 102R | 103U | | 104W | 105Z | 106R | 107M | 108D | 109A | 110M | 111B | 112S | 113aa | 114F |
| | 115F | 116C | | 117M | | 118E | 119V | 120P | 121Z | 122aa | 123J | | 124E | 125C | 126aa | 127N | 128V | | 129W | 130T | | 131U | 132C | 133G | 134N |
| 135P | 136aa | 137S | | 138M | 139D | 140S | 141P | | 142N | 143J | 144bb | 145aa | | 146T | 147J | 148L | 149K | 150H | 151C | 152S | | 153aa | 154C | 155D | 156Y | 157M |
| 158L | | 159P | 160aa | | 161I | 162bb | 163V | | 164D | 165K | 166F | | 167Q | 168G | 169N | | 170Y | 171bb | 172N | | 173V | 174L | 175S | 176M | 177bb | 178P |
| | 179F | 180O | 181H | 182aa | 183bb | | 184S | | 185A | 186F | 187W | 188Q | 189V | 190aa | 191O | | 192O | 193bb | 194J | 195Y | | 196W | 197P | 198G | | 199M |
| 200C | 201Y | 202F | 203I | | 204F | 205W | | 206J | 207R | 208M | 209G | 210D | 211Y | 212bb | 213T | 214L | | 215X | 216E | 217H | | 218O | 219U | 220H | 221M |

**P** Small brush (5, 5)

__ __ __ __ __ __ __ __ __ __
40 197 159 94 141 135 178 54 24 120

**Q** At an oblique angle

__ __ __ __ __
167 188 41 15 42

**R** 1974 Mel Brooks' movie — *Frankenstein*

__ __ __ __ __
207 68 102 106 50

**S** Went over the top with a role

__ __ __ __ __ __ __ __ __
112 84 93 44 184 140 175 152 137

**T** Winkler role from Happy Days (after "The")

__ __ __ __
146 130 19 213

**U** Knight's wear

__ __ __ __ __
219 103 131 62 2

**V** Paul Revere's two options (4, 3, 3)

__ __ __ __ __ __ __ __ __ __
76 119 128 16 189 6 45 21 163 173

**W** Camp counselor's final call (6, 3)

__ __ __ __ __ __ __ __ __
86 77 104 37 129 187 205 66 196

**X** Constant; loyal

__ __ __ __ __ __ __ __
99 43 59 64 215 28 74 13

**Y** "Mary had a —" ( 6, 4)

__ __ __ __ __ __ __ __ __ __
211 87 170 26 14 20 156 97 195 201

**Z** Blue pencil

__ __ __ __
105 81 121 36

**AA** Type of bank (7, 3, 4)

__ __ __ __ __ __ __ __ __
153 136 126 5 113 190 60 39 160 145

__ __ __ __
122 101 12 182

**BB** Afraid of water

__ __ __ __ __ __ __ __ __ __
162 10 183 193 144 61 171 177 75 212

__
11

# Part IV
## The Part of Tens

**The 5th Wave**          By Rich Tennant

"Oscar Mellen's a great puzzler, but he's never been able to attend this convention primarily because there's no common letter in his first and last name."

## In this part . . .

I give you tips to help make you a better solver, faster. I also give you several lists of repeaters that should help you solve some clues more easily.

# Chapter 1
# Ten Keys to Crosswordese

*1*n this chapter, I let you in on some quick tips that can give you a leg-up in the grid.

## Getting a Clue

Crosswords are neat little packages with clues numbered to match their location in the grid. As a rule, clues fall into the following six general categories:

✔ **Missing word:** Such as "Like — of bricks" (A TON).

✔ **Proper names:** For example, "Author Ferber" (EDNA).

✔ **Synonyms:** These are very straightforward, such as "Dessert choice" (PIE).

✔ **Foreign words:** Constructors often use a city name to tip you off that the entry is a foreign word, such as "Madrid matron" (SENORA).

✔ **Wordplay:** Most of the time a question mark at the end of a clue signals you that the clue involves wordplay, such as "Flat piece of paper?" (LEASE).

✔ **Themes:** Of course, themes vary from puzzle to puzzle. Just remember that theme clues are usually the longest clues in the grid.

When solving, look for types of clues (following the sequence of clue types given in the preceding list) rather than tackling the clues by number sequence.

Crosswordese allows for grid entries to include more than one word in a sequence, as in "Like A TON of bricks." Within the grid, entries of two words are not separated by a black square.

# *Keeping Some Repeaters in Your Pocket*

You see certain words, called *repeaters,* over and over again in crosswords. Constructors use repeaters a lot because their letters work well when building a crossword. Repeaters have certain common traits, including the following:

- ✔ They often include the letters A and E
- ✔ They often alternate vowels and consonants
- ✔ They don't include hard-to-use letters like J, Q, and Z
- ✔ They usually run three to five letters

While puzzle constructors once favored heraldic or scientific terms for repeaters, modern repeaters are more likely to derive from the world of computers ("PC key" = ESC), TV ("Carson successor" = LENO), or even brand names ("Sportswear brand" = NIKE).

Keep these useful repeaters on hand as you solve:

- ✔ **ADAR** = "Hebrew month"
- ✔ **ALAR** = "Winged"
- ✔ **ALE** = "Pub drink"
- ✔ **ANTE** = "Feed the kitty"
- ✔ **EGO** = "Freudian subject"
- ✔ **ERAT** = "Part of QED"
- ✔ **ET AL.** = "Common catch-all"
- ✔ **NEE** = "Wedding announcement word"
- ✔ **OLIO** = "Hodgepodge"
- ✔ **ORAL** = "Type of exam"

# *Strolling through the Rogue's Gallery*

Many names work well as repeaters. Just like old friends, you get to know folks like the following on a first name basis as you work crosswords:

- ✔ **ARLO** = "Folk singer Guthrie"
- ✔ **ARI** = "Jackie's ex"
- ✔ **ELLE** = "First name in supermodeling"
- ✔ **ERLE** = "Perry Mason's creator"
- ✔ **ENID** = "Playwright Bagnold"
- ✔ **ESTEE** = "First lady of cosmetics"
- ✔ **INA** = "Actress of old Balin"
- ✔ **IRA** = "Composer Gershwin"
- ✔ **OMAR** = "General Bradley"
- ✔ **OONA** = "Mrs. Chaplin"

When in doubt, try an E in the first position. The odds are in your favor, as you can see from the preceding list of top puzzle VIPs.

New names enter the puzzle lexicon everyday, such as "Olympic medalist Lipinski" for TARA. Keeping up on current events can help your puzzle prowess.

# Catching Some Frequent Flyers

You see the same birds landing in the grid if you take to crossword bird-watching. Here are some of the grids most popular egg layers:

- ✓ ANI
- ✓ ARA
- ✓ EMU
- ✓ ERN
- ✓ IBIS
- ✓ LOON
- ✓ MOA
- ✓ RAIL
- ✓ SORA
- ✓ TERN

"Flightless bird" is a frequent clue for EMU and MOA. The others answer to "Sea bird" or the crosswordese clue "Boardwalk visitor."

# Fishing for Prefixes

Because puzzles favor entries with few letters, prefixes make ideal crossword fodder. (A prefix, as you know, is the syllable attached to the beginning of a word to alter its meaning.) You can expect to see the following prefixes attaching themselves regularly to words in the grid:

- ✓ **ECTO** = "Prefix meaning outer"
- ✓ **ENDO** = "Prefix meaning inner"
- ✓ **EPI** = "Prefix with dermis"
- ✓ **META** = "Prefix with physical"
- ✓ **NEO** = "Prefix meaning new"
- ✓ **OMNI** = "Prefix meaning all"
- ✓ **POLY** = "Prefix meaning many"
- ✓ **TELE** = "Prefix with gram or graph"

In older puzzles, the standard clue for a prefix includes a tag such as "All: prefix" for OMNI. Nowadays, clues often disguise a prefix entry as a "starter," "introduction" or "lead-in," as in the clue "Physical introduction" for the entry META or "Present opener" for OMNI. Disguising a prefix entry is a nice way of combining a chuckle with a clever presentation of a repeater.

If a clue is particularly tricky, the constructor may add a question mark to tip you off to upcoming wordplay, such as "Start to form?" for the entry UNI.

# *Tracking Tailgaters*

Suffixes are also popular puzzle repeaters. Among the top contenders are the following:

- ✔ **ANA** = "Literary suffix"
- ✔ **ANE** = "Scientific suffix"
- ✔ **ENCE** = "Differ attachment"
- ✔ **ENE** = "Scientific suffix"
- ✔ **ESE** = "Language suffix"
- ✔ **ETTE** = "Major attachment"
- ✔ **ISM** = "Believer's ending"
- ✔ **ITE** = "Attachment to Brooklyn" or "Native: suffix"
- ✔ **OSE** = "Sugar: suffix"
- ✔ **OTIC** = "Suffix relating to the ear"
- ✔ **STER** = "Young follower"

The words "trailer," "follower," "ender," and "ending" in a clue may signal that the entry is a suffix.

# *Taking the Proper "Short" Cuts*

Abbreviations provide a rich source of puzzle repeaters. A handy cross section of puzzle-friendly abbreviations include the following:

- ✔ **ACAD** = "Part of USNA"
- ✔ **ANAT** = "Med. school course"
- ✔ **ATM** = "Bank convenience: abbr."
- ✔ **BIOL** = "Science course: abbr."
- ✔ **ECON** = "MBA's subject"
- ✔ **ETA** = "Airport abbr."
- ✔ **ET AL** = "List ender"
- ✔ **MOS** = "Calendar pages: abbr."
- ✔ **PTA** = "School org."
- ✔ **SEC** = "Part of a minute: abbr."
- ✔ **SEN** = "DC VIP"

An abbreviation within the clue (for example, "DC VIP" for SEN or "Doctor's org." for AMA) alerts you that the entry is an abbreviation. Sometimes, the term "short" or "shortened" indicates an abbreviation, as in "Short life story" for BIO.

# Eeee's Does It

With so many "E words" in the realm of repeaters, it wouldn't hurt to keep the following useful ones in mind:

- **EEL** = "Moray" or "Slippery one"
- **EON(S)** = "Long time"
- **EPA** = "Gov't watchdog"
- **EPEE** = "Dueling sword" or "Fencing weapon"
- **ERA** = "Memorable time" or "Slice of time"
- **ERIE** = "One of HOMES" or "Great Lake"
- **ETA** = "Letter from Greece"
- **EROS** = "God of love"
- **EST** = "Superlative suffix"
- **ETNA** = "Sicilian volcano" or "Lab burner"

# Putting on the Constructor's Cap

Repeaters are the necessary building blocks of crosswords, a boring fact of life to the constructor. To enhance the challenge the constructor goes to great lengths to disguise an everyday repeater. It shouldn't surprise you to come across a clue like "Florentine flower" for ARNO. No, the river hasn't spawned a new blossom. But constructors have created a new synonym for river: FLOW-ER.

Expect wordplay, especially where repeaters are involved. All is not always what it seems at first glance!

# Chapter 2
# Ten Languages for the Grid

*W*hen you travel the world in puzzles, you end up stopping in the same ports of call. In an effort to expand the domain of shorter puzzle entries, constructors borrow words from foreign languages. Over time, many of the shorter foreign words have joined the lexicon of "repeaters" (common crossword entries). In fact, you develop an ear for a whole host of foreign terms even if you never leave the comfort of your solving chair! I acquaint you with the most popular of these repeaters in this chapter.

## Filling in the French

*Bonjour,* solvers! In the following list of common French repeaters, notice the great way French repeaters tend to end on a vowel:

✔ **AMI** = "French friend"

✔ **A MOI** = "Mine, in Paris"

✔ **CHERI** = "French endearment"

✔ **ECU** = "Old French coin"

✔ **ETE** = "French season"

✔ **ETRE** = "French I verb"

✔ **ICI** = "Here, in Le Havre"

✔ **NEE** = "Wedding announcement word"

✔ **NICE** = "French town"

✔ **ROI** = "French king"

✔ **SOU** = "Worthless French coin"

In earlier days, clues openly identified French words by using the abbreviation "Fr.," as in

"Friend: Fr." for AMI. Nowadays, constructors use a well-known French name or town as a touchstone to convey the same fact — for example, "Pierre's friend" or "Friend in Paris."

The two French abbreviations in the repeater lexicon answer to "French miss" (MLLE) and "French Mrs." (MME).

# Say It in Spanish

*Esta,* that is! Make yourself at home with these top Spanish-language repeaters:

- ✔ **ANO** = "Year, in the Yucatan"
- ✔ **CASA** = "Home, in Havana"
- ✔ **ESTA** = "Como — usted?"
- ✔ **OLE** = "Cheer at the corrida"
- ✔ **ORO** = "Spanish gold"
- ✔ **PESO** = "Cash, in Cancun"
- ✔ **RIO** = "Grande, for one"
- ✔ **SALA** = "Room in a casa"
- ✔ **TACO** = "Mexican meal"
- ✔ **TORO** = "Matador's opponent" or "Spanish bull"

Spanish names in clues tips you off to a Spanish entry, as in "Pedro's pop" for PADRE rather than the old fashioned "Father: Sp."

# Solving, Italian-Style

Italian contributes many musical terms and noodle dishes to the crossword lexicon, as you can see in the following list of repeaters taken from Italian:

- ✔ **ALLE** = "— breve: music"
- ✔ **ARIA** = "Operatic solo"
- ✔ **CIAO** = "Greeting, in Genoa"
- ✔ **CODA** = "Musical ending"
- ✔ **LARGO** = "Musical direction"
- ✔ **LIRA** = "Money, in Milan"
- ✔ **PASTA** = "Spaghetti, e.g."
- ✔ **PENNE** = "Pasta dish"
- ✔ **TRE** = "Three, in Torino"
- ✔ **ZITI** = "Pasta dish"

References to Italian cities in clues means Italian language entries. Popular possibilities include Rome and Milan, as in "Money in Milan" for LIRA.

# Going German

*Ach Du Lieber!* Indeed, one of German's biggest contributions to puzzles is that first syllable ACH ("German exclamation"). Other contributions include the following:

- **DANKE** = "Teutonic thanks"
- **DREI** = "Three, in Berlin"
- **EINE** = " — *Kleine Nachtmusik* (Mozart)"
- **FRAU** = "German woman"
- **GRAF** = "German nobleman"
- **HERR** = "German gentleman" or "Mister, in Munich"
- **NIE** = "Never, in Bonn"
- **VIER** = "Four, German style"
- **VON** = "German title"

Several words answer to the clue "German article," including DAS, DER, or EIN, and EINE.

# Classical Crosswords

So-called dead languages are alive and well in a cozy puzzle niche. Latin, especially, offers many familiar repeaters like the following:

- **ALAE** = "Wings, to Caesar"
- **AMO** = "Latin I verb"
- **AMAT** = "Amo, amas, —"
- **ANNO** = "Part of A.D."
- **ARS** = "— longa, vita brevis"
- **AVE** = "Hail, to Caesar"
- **ERAT** = "Part of Q.E.D."
- **ET AL** = "Common catch-all"
- **ETC** = "List ender"
- **SINE** = "— qua non"

Roman numerals also offer a nice way to combine consonants in unusual ways. You see clues like "Medieval Roman date" for an entry like MLIV. When a clue calls for a Roman date, use the following "conversion table" to solve the clue:

- **I** = 1

- ✔ **V** = 5
- ✔ **X** = 10
- ✔ **L** = 50
- ✔ **C** = 100
- ✔ **D** = 500
- ✔ **M** = 1,000

# Solving Letter by Letter

Some languages offer single letters from their alphabets as neat crossword entries. Ancient Greek is tops in this category. The clue "Letter from Greece" may call for any of the following entries:

- ✔ ALPHA
- ✔ BETA
- ✔ CHI
- ✔ ETA
- ✔ IOTA
- ✔ RHO
- ✔ TAU
- ✔ PSI
- ✔ PHI

Keep in mind that the Greek alphabet begins with ALPHA and ends with OMEGA.

The Hebrew alphabet is also a source of many repeaters. Its letters offer many possibilities in the grid, such as the following:

- ✔ MEM
- ✔ NUN
- ✔ TAV
- ✔ VAV
- ✔ YOD

Two top Hebrew repeaters are HORA as in "Israeli folkdance" and TOV as in the missing word clue "Mazel —!"

# Scottish Sayings

Okay — Scottish may not be a foreign tongue in the strictest sense, but the spellings of many Scottish words make it mighty handy in the world of crosswords:

- ✔ **BRAE** = "Scottish hillside"
- ✔ **EME** = "Scottish uncle"
- ✔ **KIRK** = "Church, in Scotland"
- ✔ **GIE** = "Give, Scottish style"
- ✔ **HAE** = "Possesses, Scottish style"
- ✔ **HAGGIS** = "Scottish dish"
- ✔ **LAIRD** = "Scottish title"
- ✔ **LOCH** = "Scottish lake"
- ✔ **NAE** = "Dundee denial"
- ✔ **TASS** = "Scottish goblet"

The Scottish city of Dundee acts as the touchstone in clues calling for Scottish entries, such as "Denial in Dundee" for the entry NAE.

# Part V
# Appendixes

The 5th Wave                    By Rich Tennant

"Looks like a slow news day."

## *In this part . . .*

After you complete a puzzle (or yield to the urge to cheat on a puzzle), consult Appendix A to confirm your answers. Appendix B tells you what you need to know to solve the puzzles in Part III of this book; I include tips on solving cryptograms, acrostics, and diagramlesses.

# Appendix A
# Answers

**Puzzle 1-1: Names in Mystery**
Page 6

**Puzzle 1-3: At the Sweet Shoppe**
Page 8

**Puzzle 1-2: Strange Sightings**
Page 7

**Puzzle 1-4: P.M. Magazine**
Page 9

## Puzzle 1-5: Sob Stories
Page 10

```
C R A G   P R A M   W A S P S
L O L A   L A V A   A D L A I
A M I S   A N O N   L I O N S
W E E P I N G W I L L O W S
S O N   N E E   F O E S
    A C T   T E A R   H E M
O P E R A   D U S T   B O R E
C R Y I N G I N T H E R A I N
H I R E   I V E S   W A X E D
S E E   S L I D   S I T
    R E D S   T U N   T O G
  T H E W A I L I N G W A L L
T I A R A   O A T S   A X L E
A L T A R   N I L E   V E I N
B L E N D   S T E T   E D E N
```

## Puzzle 1-6: Hidden Grade
Page 11

```
P A N D A   A D A M   H O O D
A L O R S   D E L E   O G R E
I B E A M   O L L A   O L A F
D I S P A S S I O N A T E L Y
    E R E   S T I R
W A Y   A R S   R E A C T E D
A L A S   A M M O   B E A N O
A L L E N C O M P A S S I N G
C O T T A   K E E L   S L U E
S W A H I L I   S S T   S I S
    V E N T   O R A
P A S S E N G E R P I G E O N
O V A L   O O N A   F L A M E
G O N E   R U E R   L O V E D
O W E D   E T T E   E W E R S
```

## Puzzle 1-7: Play Ball!
Page 12

## Puzzle 1-8: Starring John Travolta
Page 13

## Puzzle 1-9: Horizontal 15s
Page 14

## Puzzle 1-10: Map Reading
Page 15

## Puzzle 1-11: Hard Stuff
Page 16

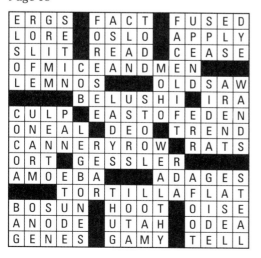

```
S O R T ■ E N L A I ■ B O D Y
C P O S ■ R O U N D ■ E R I E
H O C K ■ R O C K O F A G E S
I R K ■ C E N ■ L L A M A ■ ■
S T E W E D ■ P E A T ■ N O S
M O R E L ■ M A T T ■ D I S C
■ ■ A L A I N ■ O D E S S A
R O C K O F G I B R A L T A R
A R R E S T ■ C E S T A ■ ■
I C O N ■ E L K E ■ E N R O L
D A S ■ T R O Y ■ G R O O V E
■ S A U N A ■ P A S ■ M E A
R O C K B O T T O M ■ D A R N
E T U I ■ O H A R E ■ U N D O
A T T N ■ N E C K S ■ B O O N
```

## Puzzle 1-12: Family Affair
Page 17

```
C A R L I N ■ B O E R ■ A M T
O T O O L E ■ E R I E ■ D E E
P O P U L A R S O N G ■ I A N
A P E ■ T E E N ■ A G E N T
■ M O M E N T O F T R U T H
H E A D O N ■ A T A ■ ■
A S K E D ■ B R I C A B R A C
S T E ■ M O U N T ■ E V A
P A R A D O X E S ■ H A D E S
■ N R A ■ C I G A R S
S I S T I N E C H A P E L ■
A D L I B ■ M U I R ■ E P A
L E A ■ B R O K E N A R R O W
V A T ■ L A T E ■ E X E T E R
O L E ■ E W E S ■ Y E A S T Y
```

## Puzzle 1-13: Steinbeck Sampler
Page 18

```
E R G S ■ F A C T ■ F U S E D
L O R E ■ O S L O ■ A P P L Y
S L I T ■ R E A D ■ C E A S E
O F M I C E A N D M E N ■ ■
L E M N O S ■ O L D S A W
■ B E L U S H I ■ I R A
C U L P ■ E A S T O F E D E N
O N E A L ■ D E O ■ T R E N D
C A N N E R Y R O W ■ R A T S
O R T ■ G E S S L E R ■
A M O E B A ■ A D A G E S
■ T O R T I L L A F L A T
B O S U N ■ H O O T ■ O I S E
A N O D E ■ U T A H ■ O D E A
G E N E S ■ G A M Y ■ T E L L
```

## Puzzle 1-14: Rhyme Scheme
Page 19

```
C A R O B ■ A R C S ■ E L I E
A B A C A ■ P O O H ■ X E N A
W E S T W A R D H O ■ P I T T
S T E E L S ■ S O W ■ L A O S
■ T E S S ■ S U M O ■ ■
P O L ■ D O N O T P A S S G O
A P E S ■ R O N ■ D I N E R
N E R A ■ T W I S T ■ O A T S
T R O N A ■ O R A ■ N I N O
S A Y I T A I N T S O ■ L O N
■ T A P S ■ A S A P ■ ■
A N T I ■ A R T ■ E R A S E R
B A E Z ■ C A R O L I N E N O
E P E E ■ H E E D ■ N E R D S
L E N D ■ E L K E ■ G L E S S
```

## Puzzle 1-15: Animal House
Page 20

```
G E N A ■ O E R ■ S T A T
A L O U ■ R A G E ■ P I A N O
B I R D S O F A F E A T H E R
S A M I A M ■ D E L I ■ O A T
■ O N U S ■ R I N G E R S
T S E ■ S L O E ■ S T A ■
I O T A ■ A R T Y ■ E L E C T
C A T S I N T H E C R A D L E
S K E I N ■ S A S H ■ S A U L
■ A S P ■ N E E D ■ M E L
C O U N T E R ■ S W A T ■
A L P ■ A R E A ■ T R A L E E
F I S H N E T S T O C K I N G
E V E R T ■ A H O Y ■ E R O O
S E T S ■ G E M ■ N E S S
```

## Puzzle 1-16: Playing the Symbols
Page 21

```
H A D A ■ S N A G S ■ O H I O
O L A F ■ A E R I E ■ P O D S
L O L A ■ N U D G E ■ E R A S
S H A R P D R E S S E R S ■
T A I ■ I R O N ■ G A E L S
■ E L A N ■ S L O S H E D
U S D A ■ X I I ■ I V S
N A T U R A L B L O N D E
C D C ■ J R S ■ N O E L
H E R D E R S ■ S E T S ■
A R I E S ■ S E R A ■ O K S
■ F L A T C H A M P A G N E
L A I T ■ A L I B I ■ F L E A
I N C A ■ S I R E N ■ R E E L
P I E S ■ S P R E E ■ O D D S
```

### Puzzle 1-17: Acceleration
Page 22

### Puzzle 1-18: It's About Time
Page 23

### Puzzle 1-19: Pulitzer Prose
Page 24

### Puzzle 1-20: Two of a Kind
Page 25

### Puzzle 1-21: Women's Lit.
Page 26

### Puzzle 1-22: Playing the Numbers
Page 27

## Puzzle 1-23: Name Game
Page 28

```
A F T E R   E L I A S   G A B
D R I V E   P A N D A   R I O
H A L E D N A T H A N   A D Z
O U T L A Y   H A G   I P S O
C D S   C L U   N I E C E
    S T O N E D O L I V E R
M A S T   N I N   S N I D E
A S T A   S E C C O   E N I D
R I A T A   Y O N   S E T S
C A G E D N I C O L A S
  G L O O M   K I N   S T D
J O E Y   S P A   N O S I E R
O A R   P O U N D E D E Z R A
E T E   T A R O S   E M E R Y
L S D   S P E N T   S I D E S
```

## Puzzle 1-24: Applause
Page 29

```
B O S H   A C R I D   W O R M
A R E A   T H I N E   A R I A
S C A N   H A N D S O M E S T
H A N D B O O K   U P S E T
    L A M S   T U T U
A D H E R E   H A N D M A D E
P E E R   F O L I O   V I A
I L L S   P I V O T   H O O T
S T E   A L L E N   A I D E
H A N D B A L L   W A N D E R
    O U T S   M I N D
S C A N T   H A N D I C A P
H A N D S P R I N G   E L L A
A R T E   A U D I E   S I A M
G E E R   S T E A D   T O N S
```

## Puzzle 1-25: Ready, Set . . .
Page 30

```
J O S H   P H O T O   S G T S
U L N A   H O P U P   C O I L
N E A L   I R E N E   O F L A
G O G O D A N C E R   O L E G
    G A L E   E S P Y
P A G E D   M Y T H   A D S
I R O N   B L A S T O   K I T
L E T   G O A H E A D   I V E
O N O   O W N E R S   S T O P
T A P   A L A R   D U E T S
    I S L E   P E A R
S T E T   G O F O R B R O K E
T A C O   G L A I R   E Z R A
O X E N   E L I S E   A M I S
W I S E   D A R E D   L A S T
```

## Puzzle 1-26: Step into the Sixties
Page 31

```
O N M E   C A P N   A S H E N
P E E L   O L E O   S H A V E
T W I S T T I E S   T A L E S
S T R A Y   E R E   E G E S T
    P I N   D A R C
A P E M E N   S N A K E D
D A D O   S W A T H   R O D E
O L I N   T O L E T   P A G E
P E C K   I N T E R   E L A M
T O T E L L   A L T A R S
    Y A L U   B Y E
C R A B S   P R O   S P R E E
R A B A T   P O N Y T A I L S
A G I R L   E P E E   S A L T
W E T S Y   R E D S   S L E D
```

## Puzzle 1-27: What's Cooking?
Page 32

```
U S H E R   A R E A   A C T A
S I E G E   D E N S   L A I D
M L I A D   O A S T   A D A M
C O R D O N B L E U   G E R E
    N Y E T   T A R T A N
P A S S E L   O B E S E
A P P T   O M R I   S C A L P
T S A R I N A   C O N Q U E R
S E N O R   K I E V   U R G E
    G I B E R   U N E A S Y
G R E A S E   A C L U
R E I N   C A N N E L L O N I
A L D O   O L I O   L I V I D
B E E F   M E A T   A D A N O
S E R F   E S N E   H O L E S
```

## Puzzle 1-28: Dem Joints
Page 33

```
A B A S E   G R A S P   A S A
S A G A S   T E M P I   N N W
K N U C K L E B A L L   K E N
  E E R I E   S N I F F L E S
    A M A T   A N E L E
F A T   O N E S   T R Y S T S
W T H   S T A L L S   N O E L
R E U P   S O U   N C A A
M A M A   F E S T A L   K L M
I M B I B E   H E R O   S S S
  I N L E T   S R O S
C O N S O L E S   A S I A N
A N D   T E N N I S E L B O W
R T E   T R I A L   S T R I A
L O X   O S A G E   T S A R S
```

### Puzzle 1-29: Bank-ability
Page 34

| G | L | O | W | | P | O | N | G | A | | M | O | P | S |
| R | O | V | E | | I | C | E | A | X | | E | D | I | T |
| A | G | E | S | | A | T | A | R | I | | T | O | N | Y |
| F | O | R | T | U | N | R | T | E | L | L | E | R | S | |
| | | | S | N | I | T | | | L | A | O | | | |
| S | O | L | I | D | S | | D | I | A | G | R | A | M | S |
| C | R | E | D | I | T | L | I | N | E | | | L | E | I |
| A | D | D | E | D | | I | S | T | | A | P | I | E | D |
| L | E | G | | | S | E | C | O | N | D | R | A | T | E |
| P | R | E | C | I | O | U | S | | O | D | E | S | S | A |
| | | R | R | R | | | A | N | I | L | | | | |
| | S | Q | U | A | R | E | A | C | C | O | U | N | T | S |
| B | A | U | M | | O | R | O | N | O | | D | I | A | L |
| S | L | A | B | | W | I | N | E | M | | E | C | R | U |
| C | A | D | S | | S | E | E | D | S | | S | E | A | M |

### Puzzle 1-30: Home Teams
Page 35

| M | E | S | A | | V | E | R | V | E | | T | R | A | M |
| E | X | I | T | | A | V | A | I | L | | H | A | R | E |
| S | P | A | T | | C | A | L | I | F | O | R | N | I | A |
| H | O | M | E | M | A | D | E | | | P | E | D | A | L |
| | | | M | A | T | E | | S | H | E | A | | | |
| E | L | A | P | S | E | | S | P | A | R | T | A | N | S |
| N | O | R | T | H | D | A | K | O | T | A | | R | O | E |
| D | I | R | S | | | D | I | D | | | P | E | O | N |
| E | R | A | | R | H | O | D | E | I | S | L | A | N | D |
| D | E | S | P | A | I | R | S | | N | O | O | S | E | S |
| | | | A | D | E | N | | S | T | A | T | | | |
| A | M | A | T | I | | S | H | O | R | T | E | N | S | |
| W | A | S | H | I | N | G | T | O | N | | I | D | O | L |
| A | L | T | O | | I | N | A | N | E | | N | E | R | O |
| Y | E | A | S | | L | U | R | E | D | | G | N | A | W |

### Puzzle 1-31: Northern Exposure
Page 36

| C | A | T | E | R | | D | E | R | | D | E | F | A | T |
| A | L | I | C | E | | I | D | A | | E | R | A | S | E |
| P | I | L | O | T | | S | I | D | | M | I | T | E | R |
| E | V | E | | A | R | C | T | I | C | O | C | E | A | N |
| S | E | D | A | K | A | | S | O | O | N | | | | |
| | | | R | E | B | S | | | N | E | I | M | A | N |
| A | R | A | L | | B | L | O | T | | S | N | A | R | E |
| S | I | B | E | R | I | A | N | H | U | S | K | I | E | S |
| K | L | I | N | E | | P | E | E | L | | I | N | S | T |
| S | L | E | E | V | E | | E | T | T | E | | | | |
| | | | E | L | A | L | | R | A | R | E | S | T | |
| P | O | L | A | R | I | C | E | C | A | P | | V | A | R |
| S | M | I | L | E | | U | N | O | | E | M | I | L | E |
| S | A | T | I | N | | T | I | E | | R | A | T | T | Y |
| T | R | E | A | T | | E | N | D | | S | T | A | Y | S |

### Puzzle 1-32: B List
Page 37

| B | A | I | T | S | | S | T | E | M | | A | B | C | S |
| A | S | C | A | P | | M | E | N | U | | R | E | A | L |
| B | I | O | L | O | G | I | C | A | L | | I | R | M | A |
| S | A | N | | R | U | T | H | | D | I | S | N | E | Y |
| | | | E | T | A | H | | S | O | R | T | A | | |
| R | O | B | B | E | R | | S | P | O | R | A | D | I | C |
| A | H | E | A | D | | B | E | A | N | S | | E | L | A |
| K | A | H | N | | P | A | N | T | S | | S | T | O | P |
| E | R | A | | P | R | I | Z | E | | F | A | T | S | O |
| D | E | V | A | L | E | R | A | | C | A | R | E | E | N |
| | | | I | L | I | A | D | | H | A | D | A | | |
| P | R | O | T | E | M | | D | O | S | E | | A | I | L |
| R | A | R | E | | B | E | R | N | A | D | O | T | T | E |
| O | M | A | R | | L | A | N | E | | T | R | E | E | S |
| P | A | L | S | | E | R | O | S | | O | B | E | S | E |

### Puzzle 1-33: Fish Stories
Page 38

| E | M | I | T | | T | S | H | I | | R | E | P | O | |
| S | O | L | E | M | A | T | E | S | | E | P | O | D | E |
| S | A | L | M | O | N | A | R | S | | V | E | R | D | I |
| | | | P | O | S | T | | U | S | U | R | P | E | R |
| E | S | S | E | N | | I | B | E | T | | G | O | R | E |
| R | O | C | S | | I | C | E | | R | A | N | I | | |
| A | N | A | T | | B | A | T | | A | D | E | S | T | E |
| S | I | L | | E | E | L | W | I | N | D | | E | E | N |
| E | C | L | A | I | R | | E | N | G | | A | F | R | O |
| | | O | M | N | I | | E | S | E | | P | U | R | L |
| A | L | P | O | | A | T | N | O | | A | P | L | E | A |
| S | O | P | R | A | N | O | | L | O | N | E | | | |
| I | D | I | O | M | | S | M | E | L | T | A | R | A | T |
| T | E | N | S | E | | C | O | N | G | E | R | S | P | Y |
| | N | E | O | N | | A | C | T | A | | S | T | E | R |

### Puzzle 1-34: Hidden Assets
Page 39

| B | E | R | E | T | | A | C | L | U | | P | A | L | L |
| A | C | A | R | E | | S | P | A | N | | O | L | E | O |
| J | O | H | N | N | Y | C | A | S | H | | S | L | A | B |
| A | N | S | | P | O | I | S | | I | N | T | A | K | E |
| | | | G | I | G | I | | A | N | T | I | | | |
| H | A | V | A | N | A | | N | I | G | H | T | C | A | P |
| A | M | I | R | S | | R | I | D | E | | N | O | D | E |
| R | O | S | Y | | B | O | N | E | S | | O | N | E | L |
| T | U | T | U | | A | G | E | S | | S | T | I | L | T |
| E | R | A | S | U | R | E | S | | P | I | E | C | E | S |
| | | | B | R | I | T | | H | O | E | S | | | |
| A | D | R | O | I | T | | P | E | N | S | | E | A | U |
| S | E | A | N | | O | V | E | R | S | T | O | C | K | S |
| A | C | I | D | | N | I | L | E | | A | R | R | I | D |
| P | O | D | S | | E | V | E | S | | S | A | U | N | A |

## Puzzle 1-35: Code Names
Page 40

```
E G O . A D A M E . S H E A
A R A W . L E H A R . P I T S
D A L L A S M A T R I A R C H
O S O . Y O U . R E T R O .
P E R S E . R H O D A . H A Y
T R E E . B R A N . R I F E
. P E L E G . B E A T E N
. A U T H O R G L A S G O W
I N G E S T . L I B E L .
C O A T . P E K E . A M O S
I N N . E L I D E . I N E R T
. D A R I N . W E T . T I O
C L A R I N E T I S T S H A W
O I N K . E R O S E . L O N E
B E S S . N O V E L . O D A
```

## Puzzle 1-36: Brain Power
Page 41

```
E R G S . B Y E . T O W E L
A E R O . I R A N . O L I V E
S M A R T C A R D . R E S I N
T I P T O E . D E L E . E L S
. T H E T A S . D O R S A
. D E G A S . S O C C E R
A B S . M E R E S T . A R N O
C O A L S . D R U . F R E T S
T O G A . M A I T R E . S O S
S T E V I E . F R O S T .
. B A N A L . A S S E S S
V A R . K N O T . A U R A T E
E X U D E . S H A R P E Y E D
R I S E R . E E L Y . S I N E
A S H E S . R E F . A T O N
```

## Puzzle 1-37: I'll Take Manhattan
Page 42

```
C H A P . S O F A S . B E E T
E A S E . A R I S E . O S S A
E R I N . L I N E R . R A S P
. M A D I S O N A V E N U E .
. U R A L . E S E .
B I B L E . E L M . P O S S E
A M O U N T . E R A . H U N
G A R M E N T D I S T R I C T
E G O . T A G . P I E R R E
L E N D S . R E F . A F T E R
. O A S . A T R I .
. S T O C K E X C H A N G E .
S H A D . E L M E R . E L L E
H A I L . E L A T E . R E B A
O G L E . T A S S E . Y E A R
```

## Puzzle 1-38: Every Which Way
Page 43

```
G A B . F L E E . S H O V E
A D O . L A T T E . R U L E D
L E O . U P A N D C O M I N G
A N K L E . L A I R . D O T E
. R I N K . T E A R .
. L E F T I N T H E L U R C H
L I V E . L E E . E M E R Y
A M I . A T T E N D S . A I M
I B E A M . T E A . O P E N
D O W N I N T H E D U M P S
. O D O R . E P E E .
C L O T . R A I D . E N A C T
R I G H T A S R A I N . R O W
I D L E D . H E R O D . E L I
B O E R S . S E N S . D A N
```

## Puzzle 1-39: Lost in New York
Page 44

```
S T A B . F E L L S . B A C H
H O L E . A X I A L . E C H O
A F A R . L I A N A . E R A T
Q U E E N S T R A N S F E R .
. T E E . I T A .
A I D . E T T A . S U P P E R
C R O W . T I R E . N O O S E
H E L E N O F S Y R A C U S E
E N E R O . F O R E . O R E S
S E D E R S . N E S T . S S E
. M A T . T E A .
. A L B A N Y B I L L C O D Y
F R A U . E L A T E . O B O E
R A Z Z . S E L E S . R I L L
I N E Z . T R I M S . N E L L
```

## Puzzle 1-40: Name Game
Page 45

```
P E A T . A G A T E . A V I D
E L M O . S A L A D . K E N O
E L M E R S R I C E . I R O N
P E O N I E S . O N E M A N S
. A N N . T U B S .
A R T I S T S . C A R O M E D
P O O L E . H A R T E . I V E
A L M S . C A N O E . G L E N
R E M . C A R T S . A R E N T
T O Y L A N D . S A D I S T S
. S E A N . R I D .
T I T A N I C . E G O I S T S
A G U N . B I L L Y S R O S E
T O N E . A T O L L . O M A N
I R E D . L E A S E . N E R D
```

## Puzzle 1-41: Store Signs, for Starters
Page 46

## Puzzle 1-44: Valentine's Day Trio
Page 49

## Puzzle 1-42: Rhyme Time
Page 47

## Puzzle 1-45: Smorgasbord
Page 50

## Puzzle 1-43: Stacks of Seven
Page 48

## Puzzle 1-46: Two Words in One
Page 51

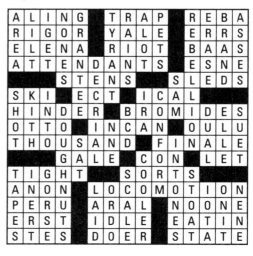

## Puzzle 1-47: Knickknacks
Page 52

| A | F | A | R |   | A | N | T | I |   |   | S | H | E | A |
| L | A | M | A |   | L | O | O | N |   | S | E | A | M | S |
| B | R | I | C | A | B | R | A | C |   | T | A | L | C | S |
| S | E | N | I | L | E |   | D | A | T | A |   | F | E | E |
|   |   |   | N | A | R | K |   | W | I | D | G | E | T |   |
| B | E | R | G |   | I | A | N |   | A | R | I | A |   |   |
| A | C | E |   | S | C | R | O | D |   | W | A | L | E | S |
| W | H | A | T | C | H | A | M | A | C | A | L | L | I | T |
| L | O | S | E | R |   | T | A | L | L | Y |   | O | R | E |
|   | S | E | A | L |   | D | E | E |   | A | N | E | W |   |
| T | H | I | N | G | Y |   |   | S | N | A | P |   |   |   |
| R | A | G |   | G | E | A | R |   | C | L | A | U | S | E |
| A | N | N | U | L |   | D | O | O | H | I | C | K | E | Y |
| P | O | E | S | Y |   | Z | O | N | E |   | H | E | A | R |
| S | I | D | E |   |   | E | K | E | D |   | E | S | T | E |

## Puzzle 1-48: Popular Pairs
Page 53

| H | A | S | T | E |   | S | A | P | S |   | H | A | F | T |
| A | N | T | E | D |   | E | L | I | E |   | I | D | A | E |
| S | T | A | R | E |   | L | A | N | E |   | G | I | B | E |
| H | I | T | A | N | D | M | I | S | S |   | H | O | L | M |
|   |   |   | I | R | A |   | A | B | A | S | E | S |   |   |
| I | N | D | U | C | E |   | R | O | W | A | N |   |   |   |
| N | E | A | P |   | W | A | I | F |   | I | D | E | A | L |
| C | A | R | A | T |   | D | O | I |   | L | L | A | M | A |
| A | R | E | N | A |   | A | T | T | A |   | O | V | E | N |
|   |   |   | D | R | A | M | S |   | L | O | W | E | N | D |
| A | T | B | A | T | S |   | A | P | R |   |   |   |   |   |
| D | R | U | B |   | T | O | U | C | H | A | N | D | G | O |
| D | I | N | O |   | E | L | S | A |   | T | I | E | I | N |
| E | T | T | U |   | R | E | E | S |   | O | C | A | L | A |
| R | E | S | T |   | N | O | S | E |   | R | E | R | A | N |

## Puzzle 1-49: Paging Mrs. Malaprop
Page 54

| A | R | A | B |   | S | A | M | A | R |   | C | A | Y | S |
| W | I | L | L |   | C | L | O | S | E |   | A | M | O | K |
| N | O | T | O |   | R | E | A | C | H |   | R | E | L | Y |
|   | T | O | W | N | O | F | T | H | E | T | A | L | K |   |
|   |   | S | O | L |   |   |   | A | S | T | I |   |   |   |
| A | R | A |   | E | L | M | E | R | E |   | O | N | A |   |
| N | A | V | E | L |   | O | A | T | S |   | A | R | I | D |
| G | R | A | S | S | I | N | T | H | E | S | N | A | K | E |
| R | E | N | T |   | M | E | T | A |   | O | N | T | O | P |
| Y | E | T |   | O | P | T |   | N | U | N |   | E | N | T |
|   |   | G | E | A | R |   |   |   | P | I | G |   |   |   |
|   | W | A | L | K | O | F | T | H | E | C | O | C | K |   |
| D | I | R | T |   | P | R | E | E | N |   | R | O | L | L |
| U | N | D | O |   | E | A | R | E | D |   | S | E | E | M |
| B | E | E | N |   | R | E | A | D | S |   | E | D | E | N |

## Puzzle 1-50: Same Starters
Page 55

| M | U | N | I |   |   | B | R | A | G |   | A | B | A | B |
| A | L | A | V | A |   | R | U | S | E |   | V | O | T | E |
| O | U | T | O | F | S | I | G | H | T |   | A | B | L | E |
|   | L | A | R | I | A | T | S |   | S | A | N | T | A |   |
| E | A | T |   | R | U | T |   | D | I | S | T | A | N | T |
| S | T | O | R | E | D |   | L | A | N | K |   | I | T | O |
| P | E | R | K |   | F | O | R | T | E |   | L | A | Y |   |
|   |   | O | U | T | O | F | T | O | W | N |   |   |   |   |
| A | D | E |   | M | O | L | T | S |   | O | M | E | R |   |
| G | E | L |   | B | O | D | Y |   | S | T | R | I | P | E |
| O | M | E | L | E | T | S |   | F | U | R |   | S | I | X |
|   | E | V | E | R | T |   | A | R | R | E | S | T | S |   |
| T | S | A | R |   | O | U | T | O | F | S | O | R | T | S |
| U | N | T | O |   | O | P | E | C |   | S | W | A | L | E |
| B | E | E | T |   | T | A | N | K |   | S | L | E | W |   |

## Puzzle 1-51: Members Only
Page 56

| M | A | T | T |   | D | E | B | I | T |   | S | T | O | P |
| A | L | A | E |   | E | R | A | S | E |   | R | U | S | E |
| S | A | N | E |   | B | I | L | L | S |   | A | R | C | S |
| H | I | G | H | S | O | C | I | E | T | Y |   | K | A | T |
|   |   | E | E | N |   |   | S | E | E | K | E | R | S |   |
| R | A | C | E | C | A | R | S |   | D | A | L | Y |   |   |
| O | A | R |   | T | I | N | E |   | R | E | C | T | O |   |
| T | H | O | R |   | R | A | D | A | R |   | E | L | E | V |
| A | S | P | I | C |   | E | L | E | M |   | U | T | E |   |
|   | C | O | R | E |   | R | E | M | E | M | B | E | R |   |
| E | D | I | T | O | R | S |   | O | N | A |   |   |   |   |
| A | I | R |   | C | R | E | D | I | T | U | N | I | O | N |
| T | E | C | H |   | A | N | O | D | E |   | I | N | R | E |
| U | G | L | I |   | T | A | L | E | S |   | A | C | E | D |
| P | O | E | M |   | A | T | E | S | T |   | C | A | S | S |

## Puzzle 1-52: Double-O
Page 57

| B | O | S | S |   | D | A | M | E |   | V | A | L | I | D |
| L | O | N | I |   | W | R | A | P |   | O | P | E | R | A |
| E | N | I | D |   | E | N | Y | A |   | O | R | E | A | D |
| W | A | T | E | R | L | O | O |   | A | D | O | R | N | S |
|   |   |   | W | I | T |   | R | A | D | O | N |   |   |   |
| C | A | R | A | T |   | M | A | R | I | O |   | L | A | S |
| A | G | I | L | E |   | A | L | A | E |   | P | I | T | T |
| J | A | C | K | S | O | O |   | B | U | G | A | B | O | O |
| U | T | E | S |   | V | I | C | I |   | A | R | E | N | A |
| N | E | D |   | T | E | S | L | A |   | V | A | L | E | T |
|   |   |   | S | A | N | T | O |   | G | E | L |   |   |   |
| C | A | D | E | T | S |   | B | A | L | L | Y | H | O | O |
| E | R | E | C | T |   | A | B | L | E |   | Z | E | B | U |
| L | E | N | T | O |   | M | E | S | A |   | E | R | I | C |
| L | A | S | S | O |   | P | R | O | M |   | D | A | S | H |

## Puzzle 1-53: Literally Speaking
Page 58

| C | O | L | A | S | ■ | S | H | E | A | R | ■ | W | A | S |
| A | B | O | R | T | ■ | K | A | R | M | A | ■ | A | C | E |
| L | O | O | K | Y | O | U | L | E | A | P | ■ | T | C | U |
| ■ | ■ | K | ■ | A | M | B | L | E | ■ | R | I | D | E | R | S |
| S | P | A | N | I | E | L | ■ | ■ | F | E | D | O | R | A | S |
| N | U | R | S | E | D | ■ | C | U | T | L | E | T | ■ |
| A | R | R | A | S | ■ | M | A | R | T | Y | ■ | H | A | D |
| K | E | E | N | ■ | H | E | L | L | O | ■ | D | E | M | O |
| E | R | S | ■ | F | A | R | M | S | ■ | C | A | D | I | Z |
| ■ | ■ | T | A | L | L | I | S | ■ | P | A | R | A | D | E |
| H | A | Y | L | O | F | T | ■ | M | I | L | K | M | E | N |
| A | E | O | L | U | S | ■ | B | E | A | D | S | ■ |
| T | R | U | ■ | N | O | O | N | S | F | R | I | D | A | Y |
| C | I | R | ■ | C | L | E | A | N | ■ | O | D | I | L | E |
| H | E | E | ■ | E | E | R | I | E | ■ | N | E | N | E | S |

## Puzzle 1-54: Lunar Sightings
Page 59

| C | H | A | P | S | ■ | M | A | T | ■ | A | L | A | E |
| R | E | P | R | O | ■ | U | N | I | V | ■ | D | E | S | I |
| A | R | S | O | N | ■ | D | E | M | I | ■ | D | O | E | R |
| M | O | O | N | A | N | D | S | I | X | P | E | N | C | E |
| ■ | ■ | T | R | Y | ■ | D | E | R | N | ■ |
| P | E | P | O | ■ | L | O | L | ■ | N | A | D | E | R |
| A | T | I | ■ | P | O | K | E | S | ■ | T | U | B | E | S |
| T | H | E | M | A | N | I | N | T | H | E | M | O | O | N |
| S | I | T | A | T | ■ | E | I | D | E | R | ■ | L | I | E |
| ■ | C | A | R | R | E | ■ | N | S | A | ■ | F | I | L | E |
| ■ | ■ | I | O | L | A | ■ | T | R | I | ■ |
| M | O | O | N | L | I | G | H | T | S | O | N | A | T | A |
| A | R | I | A | ■ | D | O | U | R | ■ | R | A | B | I | D |
| L | E | N | D | ■ | E | R | N | E | ■ | E | L | E | N | A |
| E | L | K | E | ■ | A | G | E | ■ | M | E | T | E | R |

## Puzzle 1-55: Girl Power
Page 60

| C | A | V | E | S | ■ | R | U | M | P | ■ | A | D | I | M |
| A | R | E | N | T | ■ | O | N | E | A | ■ | R | O | S | E |
| H | E | N | C | O | G | B | U | R | N | ■ | B | E | L | T |
| N | A | T | A | L | I | E | ■ | S | T | R | I | P | E | R |
| ■ | ■ | G | E | L | ■ | H | E | S | I | T | A | T | E |
| S | T | E | E | N | ■ | S | A | Y | ■ | P | E | R | ■ |
| H | E | W | S | ■ | B | A | M | ■ | Y | E | R | T | L | E |
| I | R | E | ■ | M | A | X | B | A | E | R | ■ | I | O | N |
| V | I | S | T | A | S | ■ | O | P | A | ■ | B | E | S | T |
| ■ | ■ | H | A | R | ■ | A | N | T | ■ | G | U | S | T | O |
| S | T | A | R | N | O | S | E | ■ | S | R | I | ■ |
| A | R | C | H | E | R | S | ■ | O | C | U | L | I | S | T |
| R | A | K | E | ■ | C | O | W | F | I | D | D | L | E | R |
| I | S | L | E | ■ | A | R | A | M | ■ | G | E | S | T | E |
| S | H | E | L | ■ | S | T | Y | E | ■ | E | R | A | S | E |

## Puzzle 1-56: Anatomy Lesson
Page 61

| L | A | P | P | ■ | B | E | B | O | P | ■ | O | P | A | L |
| A | B | L | E | ■ | A | R | E | C | A | ■ | R | A | T | E |
| H | E | A | R | T | B | R | E | A | K | ■ | I | R | O | N |
| A | L | I | ■ | H | I | E | S | ■ | I | B | E | A | M | S |
| R | E | N | E | W | E | D | ■ | P | S | A | L | M | ■ |
| ■ | ■ | P | A | S | ■ | M | O | T | H | ■ | E | R | E |
| A | S | P | I | C | ■ | L | O | L | A | ■ | A | D | I | T |
| K | N | U | C | K | L | E | S | A | N | D | W | I | C | H |
| E | A | R | S | ■ | A | V | E | R | ■ | R | A | C | K | S |
| E | G | G | ■ | R | U | E | S | ■ | F | O | R | ■ |
| ■ | ■ | A | B | O | D | E | ■ | R | E | N | E | G | E | S |
| A | T | T | I | C | A | ■ | Z | A | N | E | ■ | E | V | A |
| R | I | O | T | ■ | B | R | A | I | N | D | R | A | I | N |
| I | N | R | E | ■ | L | A | P | S | E | ■ | A | R | T | E |
| D | A | Y | S | ■ | E | D | S | E | L | ■ | T | S | A | R |

## Puzzle 1-57: Morse Play
Page 62

| D | E | M | ■ | P | L | A | T | H | ■ | H | A | R | T | E |
| A | L | I | ■ | L | O | I | R | E | ■ | O | N | I | O | N |
| D | O | T | M | A | T | R | I | X | ■ | O | D | D | L | Y |
| O | P | T | I | C | ■ | S | A | N | K | ■ | E | D | A |
| S | E | S | T | I | N | A | ■ | N | E | A | T | ■ |
| ■ | ■ | D | A | S | H | E | D | H | O | P | E | S |
| L | A | C | R | O | S | S | E | ■ | S | T | A | R | E |
| O | L | L | A | ■ | A | N | I | T | A | ■ | E | L | I | A |
| A | T | O | N | E | ■ | D | O | C | U | M | E | N | T |
| D | O | T | T | E | D | L | I | N | E | S | ■ |
| ■ | ■ | S | L | O | E | ■ | I | D | E | A | T | E | D |
| M | E | L | ■ | L | E | A | R | ■ | A | G | E | N | A |
| A | L | I | B | I | ■ | D | A | S | H | B | O | A | R | D |
| S | L | E | E | K | ■ | E | T | H | E | L | ■ | R | O | D |
| H | E | D | G | E | ■ | D | A | Y | N | E | ■ | S | L | Y |

## Puzzle 1-58: All Rise
Page 63

| A | V | A | S | T | ■ | T | E | C | S | ■ | D | O | O | M |
| R | O | G | U | E | ■ | E | L | A | N | ■ | O | L | L | A |
| F | L | U | I | D | ■ | N | E | M | O | ■ | R | E | A | R |
| S | T | A | N | D | O | N | C | E | R | E | M | O | N | Y |
| ■ | ■ | G | E | T | ■ | T | R | E | T | S | ■ |
| A | S | A | ■ | R | A | M | ■ | A | S | H | ■ | S | A | T |
| S | I | L | O | ■ | R | A | P | ■ | I | S | T | L | E |
| S | T | A | N | D | U | P | A | N | D | C | H | E | E | R |
| E | A | T | E | R | ■ | L | E | E | ■ | A | W | N | S |
| T | R | E | ■ | E | O | S | ■ | A | N | T | ■ | S | E | E |
| ■ | ■ | S | A | N | T | A | ■ | S | E | T | ■ |
| S | T | A | N | D | A | R | D | B | E | A | R | E | R | S |
| A | S | T | A | ■ | G | I | L | A | ■ | S | A | L | O | N |
| T | A | L | C | ■ | E | D | I | T | ■ | E | D | I | L | E |
| E | R | I | K | ■ | R | E | B | S | ■ | T | E | A | L | E |

## Puzzle 1-59: *Yo Ho Ho and a Bottle of Rum*
Page 64

| R | E | L | I | C | ■ | B | A | S | I | C | ■ | T | O | V |
| U | T | I | C | A | ■ | E | X | I | L | E | ■ | A | L | E |
| D | A | V | Y | J | O | N | E | S | L | O | C | K | E | R |
| E | L | Y | ■ | O | B | I | S | ■ | ■ | L | E | I | S | ■ |
| ■ | ■ | S | L | O | G | ■ | T | A | B | A | S | C | O | ■ |
| F | I | F | T | E | E | N | M | E | N | O | N | A | ■ | ■ |
| A | L | O | E | S | ■ | A | R | T | Y | ■ | D | O | G | ■ |
| I | S | U | P | ■ | W | A | R | N | S | ■ | K | I | W | I |
| R | A | N | ■ | M | A | L | I | ■ | ■ | S | A | V | E | S |
| ■ | ■ | D | E | A | D | M | A | N | S | C | H | E | S | T |
| T | O | E | L | E | S | S | ■ | E | A | R | N | ■ | ■ | ■ |
| A | C | R | E | ■ | ■ | Y | U | R | I | ■ | X | I | I | ■ |
| S | H | I | V | E | R | M | E | T | I | M | B | E | R | S |
| T | E | N | ■ | S | U | I | T | E | ■ | P | A | N | E | L |
| E | R | G | ■ | S | T | A | I | R | ■ | S | H | A | D | E |

## Puzzle 1-60: *Temperature's Rising*
Page 65

| C | O | P | E | S | ■ | A | G | U | E | ■ | L | I | S | P |
| P | O | R | C | H | ■ | D | O | R | A | ■ | E | N | N | A |
| O | P | E | R | A | ■ | V | E | N | T | ■ | A | L | A | R |
| ■ | ■ | S | U | M | M | E | R | S | A | N | D | E | R | S |
| A | N | S | ■ | B | A | R | ■ | ■ | B | E | E | T | L | E |
| D | O | U | B | L | E | B | O | I | L | E | R | ■ | ■ | ■ |
| A | E | R | I | E | ■ | ■ | A | C | E | D | ■ | S | S | T |
| G | L | E | N | ■ | P | I | K | E | S | ■ | P | A | T | E |
| E | S | S | ■ | Y | A | L | U | ■ | ■ | O | I | L | E | R |
| ■ | ■ | P | O | T | O | M | A | C | F | E | V | E | R | ■ |
| A | C | C | E | D | E | ■ | ■ | R | A | F | ■ | A | L | E |
| G | L | O | B | A | L | W | A | R | M | I | N | G | ■ | ■ |
| L | I | M | B | ■ | L | I | M | A | ■ | C | O | I | L | S |
| E | V | E | L | ■ | A | D | E | N | ■ | E | R | N | I | E |
| T | E | T | E | ■ | S | E | N | T | ■ | R | A | G | E | D |

## Puzzle 1-61: *Run of the Mill*
Page 66

| J | A | V | A | ■ | E | G | A | D | ■ | A | T | B | A | T |
| O | L | A | N | ■ | Z | O | N | E | ■ | B | R | A | N | D |
| C | E | N | T | ■ | R | E | D | S | ■ | H | I | L | T | S |
| O | R | D | I | N | A | R | Y | P | E | O | P | L | E | ■ |
| S | T | A | C | Y | ■ | ■ | O | R | R | ■ | R | D | A | ■ |
| E | S | L | ■ | L | U | N | A | T | E | ■ | R | O | A | D |
| ■ | ■ | P | O | P | I | N | ■ | ■ | F | O | O | T | E | ■ |
| P | L | A | I | N | C | L | O | T | H | E | S | M | E | N |
| R | A | N | T | S | ■ | D | E | B | R | A | ■ | ■ | ■ | ■ |
| A | N | A | T | ■ | F | L | E | X | O | R | ■ | P | A | T |
| M | D | L | ■ | S | R | O | ■ | ■ | E | V | A | D | E | ■ |
| ■ | C | O | M | M | O | N | C | A | R | R | I | E | R | S |
| A | R | G | U | E | ■ | D | A | N | E | ■ | S | L | I | T |
| P | A | U | L | A | ■ | O | R | E | S | ■ | A | L | A | E |
| A | B | E | L | L | ■ | N | E | W | T | ■ | S | A | N | D |

## Puzzle 1-62: *White House Residents*
Page 67

| F | I | R | S | T | ■ | S | L | A | T | ■ | H | A | F | T |
| A | R | O | A | R | ■ | I | O | N | A | ■ | E | R | I | E |
| M | I | L | L | A | R | D | F | I | L | L | M | O | R | E |
| E | S | E | ■ | V | O | L | T | ■ | K | I | S | M | E | T |
| ■ | ■ | ■ | B | E | D | E | ■ | R | A | M | ■ | A | S | H |
| L | A | S | E | R | ■ | C | I | T | E | S | ■ | ■ | ■ | ■ |
| A | G | H | A | S | T | ■ | E | L | I | ■ | A | R | I | A |
| G | R | O | V | E | R | C | L | E | V | E | L | A | N | D |
| S | A | T | E | ■ | A | L | L | ■ | E | N | T | I | R | E |
| ■ | ■ | ■ | R | A | D | I | O | ■ | ■ | T | O | N | E | S |
| I | S | M | ■ | L | E | O | ■ | P | A | I | N | ■ | ■ | ■ |
| R | E | A | G | A | N | ■ | E | A | S | T | ■ | A | W | L |
| W | I | L | L | I | A | M | M | C | K | I | N | L | E | Y |
| I | N | T | O | ■ | M | I | M | E | ■ | E | I | D | E | R |
| N | E | A | P | ■ | E | G | A | D | ■ | S | P | A | D | E |

## Puzzle 1-63: *Speaking of Star Trek*
Page 68

| S | L | A | M | ■ | E | D | A | M | ■ | D | E | N | E | S |
| N | A | V | Y | ■ | X | E | N | A | ■ | I | R | I | S | H |
| O | T | I | S | ■ | H | E | E | L | ■ | S | I | G | M | A |
| W | H | A | T | S | U | P | W | I | T | H | C | H | E | W |
| Y | E | N | ■ | O | M | S | ■ | ■ | O | U | S | T | ■ | ■ |
| ■ | ■ | ■ | D | I | E | ■ | C | A | R | P | ■ | C | Y | D |
| A | D | E | A | L | ■ | O | I | L | S | ■ | A | L | O | U |
| S | I | G | N | S | O | F | G | O | O | D | L | U | K | E |
| H | O | Y | A | ■ | P | L | A | T | ■ | R | O | B | O | T |
| E | S | P | ■ | G | E | A | R | ■ | J | O | E | ■ | ■ | ■ |
| ■ | ■ | T | H | O | R | ■ | ■ | P | E | W | ■ | A | T | A |
| L | E | I | A | W | A | K | E | A | T | N | I | G | H | T |
| A | W | A | R | E | ■ | E | L | I | S | ■ | V | E | I | L |
| R | E | N | T | S | ■ | N | I | N | A | ■ | E | N | N | A |
| A | S | S | E | T | ■ | T | E | A | M | ■ | S | A | G | S |

## Puzzle 1-64: *Watch Your Step*
Page 69

| S | T | A | R | R | ■ | C | A | M | ■ | R | I | G | O | R |
| A | U | G | I | E | ■ | U | S | A | ■ | I | N | A | N | E |
| C | R | E | S | T | ■ | B | I | N | ■ | F | U | S | E | D |
| ■ | F | R | E | U | D | I | A | N | S | L | I | P | S | ■ |
| ■ | ■ | ■ | ■ | R | O | T | ■ | ■ | P | E | T | ■ | ■ | ■ |
| S | A | V | A | N | T | ■ | O | P | E | D | ■ | O | R | E |
| A | L | I | N | E | ■ | A | R | I | A | ■ | U | T | E | S |
| H | A | R | O | D | I | S | K | C | R | A | S | H | E | S |
| I | M | U | S | ■ | N | E | A | T | ■ | G | E | E | S | E |
| B | O | S | ■ | S | T | A | N | ■ | D | A | R | R | E | N |
| ■ | ■ | ■ | O | A | R | ■ | ■ | P | E | R | ■ | ■ | ■ | ■ |
| ■ | V | I | C | T | O | R | I | A | F | A | L | L | S | ■ |
| P | A | T | T | I | ■ | A | R | S | ■ | G | O | A | L | S |
| A | L | I | E | N | ■ | G | A | T | ■ | A | G | L | E | T |
| T | E | S | T | Y | ■ | A | N | Y | ■ | R | E | A | D | Y |

## Puzzle 1-65: Name Game (Monogram)

Page 70

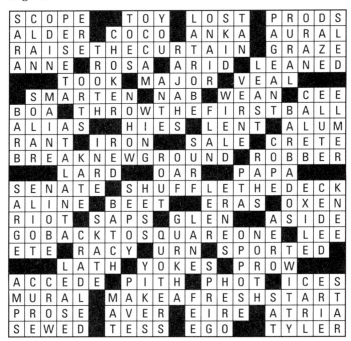

| P | E | R | M |   | C | O | E | D |   |   | O | Z | O | N | E |
| A | R | I | A |   | O | K | R | A |   |   | F | E | V | E | R |
| D | I | C | K | C | L | A | R | K |   |   | F | R | E | O | N |
| S | C | H | O | O | L |   | S | O | R | B | O | N | N | E |   |
|   |   |   | P | I | G |   | T | O | E |   |   |   |   |   |   |
| E | L | M | S |   | D | A | N | A | C | A | R | V | E | Y |   |
| N | O | A | H |   | E | G | O |   | T | E | A | S | E |   |   |
| D | U | N | E |   | S | A | L | E | M |   | A | C | T | A |   |
| E | S | T | E | S |   | A | R | A |   | C | U | E | S |   |   |
| D | Y | A | N | C | A | N | N | O | N |   | T | A | R | T |   |
|   |   |   | A | D | E |   | S | P | A |   |   |   |   |   |   |
| K | I | B | I | T | Z | E | D |   | O | R | N | A | T | E |   |
| A | D | E | P | T |   | D | R | E | W | C | A | R | E | Y |   |
| L | E | A | S | E |   | L | A | K | E |   | P | E | E | R |   |
| E | A | T | E | R |   | E | W | E | R |   | E | A | S | E |   |

## Puzzle 2-1: First Positions

Page 72

| S | C | O | P | E |   |   | T | O | Y |   | L | O | S | T |   | P | R | O | D | S |
| A | L | D | E | R |   | C | O | C | O |   | A | N | K | A |   | A | U | R | A | L |
| R | A | I | S | E | T | H | E | C | U | R | T | A | I | N |   | G | R | A | Z | E |
| A | N | N | E |   | R | O | S | A |   | A | R | I | D |   | L | E | A | N | E | D |
|   |   |   | T | O | O | K |   | M | A | J | O | R |   | V | E | A | L |   |   |   |
|   | S | M | A | R | T | E | N |   | N | A | B |   | W | E | A | N |   | C | E | E |
| B | O | A |   | T | H | R | O | W | T | H | E | F | I | R | S | T | B | A | L | L |
| A | L | I | A | S |   | H | I | E | S |   | L | E | N | T |   | A | L | U | M |   |
| R | A | N | T |   | I | R | O | N |   | S | A | L | E |   | C | R | E | T | E |   |
| B | R | E | A | K | N | E | W | G | R | O | U | N | D |   | R | O | B | B | E | R |
|   |   |   | L | A | R | D |   | O | A | R |   | P | A | P | A |   |   |   |   |   |
| S | E | N | A | T | E |   | S | H | U | F | F | L | E | T | H | E | D | E | C | K |
| A | L | I | N | E |   | B | E | E | T |   | E | R | A | S |   | O | X | E | N |   |
| R | I | O | T |   | S | A | P | S |   | G | L | E | N |   | A | S | I | D | E |   |
| G | O | B | A | C | K | T | O | S | Q | U | A | R | E | O | N | E |   | L | E | E |
| E | T | E |   | R | A | C | Y |   | U | R | N |   | S | P | O | R | T | E | D |   |
|   |   |   | L | A | T | H |   | Y | O | K | E | S |   | P | R | O | W |   |   |   |
| A | C | C | E | D | E |   | P | I | T | H |   | P | H | O | T |   | I | C | E | S |
| M | U | R | A | L |   | M | A | K | E | A | F | R | E | S | H | S | T | A | R | T |
| P | R | O | S | E |   | A | V | E | R |   | E | I | R | E |   | A | T | R | I | A |
| S | E | W | E | D |   | T | E | S | S |   | E | G | O |   | T | Y | L | E | R |   |

## *Puzzle 2-2: Driver's Ed.*

Page 74

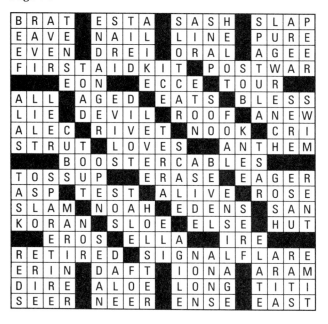

## *Puzzle 2-3: Familiar Words*

Page 76

## Puzzle 2-4: Double Features

Page 78

```
T E E M | H A N D | B A R E | H A R D
E L L E | E R T E | U S E R | O L I O
L I F E W I T H F A T H E R G O O S E
    T I R E | B L E D | O T H E R
A G A I N | M O L E | A R E A S
S L I N G B L A D E R U N N E R
H U N G | Y A L E | P E N | A O L
Y E T | C E S T | D A T E | Z A P P A
    G O B S | E E R O | S E X I E R
G R U M P Y O L D M E N I N B L A C K
R O T A T E | O N U S | D A R E
A M E N S | A G A R | M Y R A | K E G
Y E S | U M A | F I L E | P A R E
    R A G I N G B U L L D U R H A M
  E D I T H | E I R E | R E N T S
S T U N T | E S M E | T H I S
T H E S U N S H I N E B O Y S T O W N
L A T E | A S I N | G O O D | O L E O
O N O S | N E V I | G A L E | N E E D
```

## Puzzle 2-5: Get Going

Page 80

```
W H A M | S T O P | A S A P | H I D E
I O L A | T E L L | N E I L | I D O L
S P O T | E R I E | D A D E | G L U M
H I T T H E R O A D | F E A T H E R S
    R O L E | S A G A | T U T
D E L E T E | R E M A R K | G A T O R
O D E S | R O E | B E E T | I R M A
S E N S E | A G E E | R E O | L E A F
E N D | V E R A N D A | P A T I E N T
    B E D | L O G I C | S E T
E N D U R E S | S E R R A T E | S H E
B O O R | M A P | R E A D | M O L A R
B A R N | A U R A | T E A | P I L L
S H A R E | L E S S E R | N E E D L E
    U R I | S P A R | H O A R
L A M B A S T E | M A K E T R A C K S
A H A B | L I N T | S A S H | T O N E
N O N E | A R C O | E L S E | O V E N
D Y E R | M E E T | D E E R | R E E D
```

## Puzzle 2-6: Three in a Row
Page 82

| T | I | E | D | ■ | B | E | A | R | ■ | B | A | S | H | ■ | G | A | M | S |
|---|---|---|---|---|---|---|---|---|---|---|---|---|---|---|---|---|---|---|
| A | R | N | E | ■ | E | L | L | A | ■ | A | R | E | A | ■ | O | R | A | N |
| B | A | S | E | B | A | L | L | M | I | N | O | R | L | E | A | G | U | E |
| ■ | ■ | P | E | T | E | ■ | ■ | N | A | N | A | ■ | C | L | O | V | E | ■ |
| A | R | O | S | E | ■ | ■ | A | S | I | N | ■ | ■ | S | H | I | N | E | R |
| W | I | N | I | N | T | I | C | K | T | A | C | K | T | O | E | ■ | ■ | ■ |
| A | L | E | X | ■ | A | R | T | Y | ■ | ■ | L | I | D | ■ | ■ | L | B | S |
| Y | E | S | ■ | L | U | I | S | ■ | S | T | E | P | ■ | S | T | O | O | L |
| ■ | ■ | ■ | D | E | N | S | ■ | L | I | R | A | ■ | G | O | O | G | O | O |
| T | H | R | E | E | T | H | O | U | S | A | N | D | I | N | R | O | M | E |
| W | I | E | L | D | S | ■ | X | R | A | Y | ■ | I | G | G | Y | ■ | ■ | ■ |
| I | D | E | A | S | ■ | A | B | E | L | ■ | A | N | O | S | ■ | E | L | S |
| T | E | L | ■ | O | N | O | ■ | ■ | O | P | A | L | ■ | E | D | I | T | ■ |
| ■ | ■ | V | E | R | Y | W | I | D | E | S | H | O | E | S | I | Z | E | ■ |
| E | I | D | E | R | S | ■ | ■ | C | A | R | E | ■ | ■ | S | T | E | A | M |
| T | R | I | N | I | ■ | A | X | E | D | ■ | ■ | D | A | T | A | ■ | ■ | ■ |
| H | A | R | D | C | O | R | E | M | O | V | I | E | R | A | T | I | N | G |
| E | D | G | E | ■ | A | N | N | A | ■ | I | T | E | M | ■ | E | R | I | E |
| R | E | E | D | ■ | R | O | A | N | ■ | M | A | R | Y | ■ | S | E | L | L |

## Puzzle 2-7: You Bet!
Page 84

| O | M | A | R | ■ | A | L | M | S | ■ | O | S | S | A | ■ | B | A | R | E |
|---|---|---|---|---|---|---|---|---|---|---|---|---|---|---|---|---|---|---|
| R | O | L | E | ■ | R | O | A | M | ■ | A | N | E | W | ■ | U | N | I | T |
| C | A | L | M | ■ | G | O | N | E | ■ | T | A | R | A | ■ | T | O | G | A |
| A | B | S | O | L | U | T | E | L | Y | ■ | P | E | R | S | O | N | A | L |
| ■ | ■ | ■ | R | I | M | ■ | T | E | S | S | ■ | D | E | F | ■ | ■ | ■ | ■ |
| C | O | A | S | T | E | R | S | ■ | S | O | H | O | ■ | A | C | H | E | S |
| L | O | B | E | ■ | N | A | N | A | ■ | D | O | N | E | ■ | O | U | S | T |
| O | N | E | ■ | A | T | T | A | C | K | ■ | T | U | T | ■ | U | R | S | A |
| D | A | T | U | M | ■ | S | I | R | E | S | ■ | S | T | A | R | T | E | R |
| ■ | ■ | ■ | N | I | P | ■ | L | I | V | E | R | ■ | A | B | S | ■ | ■ | ■ |
| S | W | A | D | D | L | E | ■ | D | I | G | I | T | ■ | L | E | A | S | H |
| H | I | L | O | ■ | E | L | M | ■ | N | A | D | I | N | E | ■ | R | I | O |
| E | T | T | U | ■ | A | L | A | S | ■ | L | E | N | A | ■ | F | I | L | L |
| S | H | E | B | A | ■ | E | G | A | D | ■ | S | E | P | A | R | A | T | E |
| ■ | ■ | ■ | T | I | P | ■ | N | O | A | H | ■ | ■ | O | R | E | ■ | ■ | ■ |
| L | I | B | E | R | A | T | E | ■ | B | Y | A | L | L | M | E | A | N | S |
| O | V | I | D | ■ | T | E | T | E | ■ | E | R | I | E | ■ | D | R | O | P |
| G | A | L | L | ■ | I | R | I | S | ■ | N | I | N | O | ■ | O | L | E | O |
| O | N | L | Y | ■ | O | N | C | E | ■ | A | D | E | N | ■ | M | O | L | T |

## Puzzle 2-8: S-Sandwich

Page 86

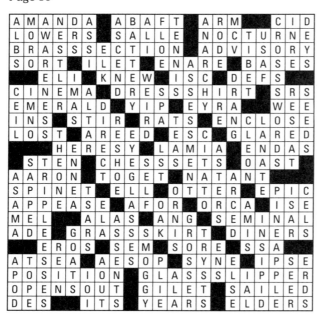

## Puzzle 2-9: As They Say

Page 88

## Puzzle 2-10: Vive Irma La Douce and Friends
Page 90

| R | O | U | T | | B | E | A | T | | M | A | L | I | | | F | L | I | P |
| E | S | N | E | | R | A | M | A | | W | A | D | E | R | | F | L | O | R | A |
| M | A | D | A | M | E | S | O | U | S | A | T | Z | K | A | | I | O | N | I | C |
| O | K | E | | A | V | I | S | | T | R | U | E | | | A | R | T | I | S | T |
| P | A | R | O | L | E | E | | F | A | I | R | | G | I | S | T | S |
| | T | H | E | T | R | O | U | B | L | E | W | I | T | H | H | A | R | R | Y |
| | D | A | I | S | | R | E | L | Y | | A | L | E | E | | M | O | U | E |
| M | A | K | O | | S | H | A | L | E | | S | T | E | R | N | O | | U | S | A |
| O | N | E | | N | O | E | L | S | | S | H | E | A | | R | O | G | E | R |
| B | A | N | D | A | N | A | S | | G | U | A | R | D | I | N | G | T | E | S | S |
| | U | N | I | T | | G | R | I | D | S | | C | O | A | T |
| S | W | E | E | T | C | H | A | R | I | T | Y | | M | I | S | N | O | M | E | R |
| I | R | A | T | E | | G | E | N | E | | L | A | N | E | S | | O | N | O |
| T | O | R | | S | C | E | N | A | S | | S | O | N | G | S | | B | U | D | D |
| E | T | N | A | | A | L | A | S | | C | H | I | T | | | L | A | S | S |
| D | E | S | P | E | R | A | T | E | C | H | A | R | A | C | T | E | R | S |
| | | P | L | A | N | E | | L | A | S | E | | L | U | M | B | E | R | S |
| A | R | A | R | A | T | | S | E | N | T | | N | E | M | O | | L | E | A |
| P | I | L | O | T | | S | O | M | E | C | A | M | E | R | U | N | N | I | N | G |
| O | G | I | V | E | | A | B | U | S | E | | E | V | I | L | | A | N | T | E |
| D | A | T | E | | C | I | T | E | | T | A | C | T | | N | E | S | S |

## Puzzle 2-11: Word Travels
Page 92

| W | A | L | K | | F | E | E | T | | M | A | I | L | | S | C | A | M |
| A | L | E | E | | L | A | M | E | | E | L | M | O | | P | E | L | E |
| S | T | A | N | | E | R | I | N | | S | E | A | T | | E | L | O | N |
| P | O | N | Y | E | X | P | R | E | S | S | | M | U | S | C | L | E | S |
| | | A | R | I | | T | E | A | R | | S | L | I | P |
| R | I | B | | A | B | C | S | | A | G | E | S | | Y | A | H | O | O |
| A | D | A | | S | L | A | I | N | | E | A | R | S | | L | O | M | A |
| M | E | L | T | | E | T | N | A | S | | M | O | A | T | | N | E | T |
| S | A | L | A | D | | E | A | V | E | S | | G | R | E | E | N | S |
| | | C | A | R | R | I | E | R | P | I | G | E | O | N |
| A | N | T | O | N | Y | | L | U | I | S | E | | T | O | R | C | H |
| R | O | E | | G | N | A | T | | M | E | L | O | N | | S | O | L | E |
| T | A | L | C | | E | D | A | M | | S | A | D | A | T | | P | A | R |
| S | H | E | L | F | | E | T | O | N | | M | E | M | O | | E | W | E |
| | G | E | A | R | | A | N | O | N | | E | N | E |
| P | I | R | A | T | E | S | | S | M | O | K | E | S | I | G | N | A | L |
| I | R | A | N | | G | O | A | T | | B | E | T | A | | R | O | M | A |
| T | I | P | S | | A | R | T | E | | L | E | A | K | | E | V | E | R |
| A | S | H | E | | L | E | E | R | | E | L | L | E | | T | A | N | K |

## Puzzle 2-12: What's Playing at the Forum?

Page 94

```
A R O N   C H A S S E   S T A B   O R A L
S A L E   R U T T E D   C A R A   S E M I
T H E X C O M M A N D M E N T S   A L A N
I S O T O P E       Y A N K E E   G A Z E
        T U R B A N   P I T     P E T E R
V E A S Y P I E C E S   C O S T A   E D S
O D I E     N I G H T   P L A T A
T E M P E R A   D E E R E   A G O N I Z E
E N S I L I N G   V I I D A Y S I N M A Y
      A F F I R M   K E G S     S E I N E
T E D     F L E A S   D E T E R   N E D
A M A N A     A R T A   D R A I N S
C I D A L M A T I A N S   O R D A I N E D
T R A V A I L   A N N U L   S E N S O R Y
      E R N E S   D E F E R     S R T A
A K A   M I X U P   X I I A N G R Y M E N
D A M E S     P O L   S A F A R I
A R A L   E A R N E R     P E O N A G E
G A Z A   T H E I I I M U S K E T E E R S
E T O N   N O M E   C A S H I N   W R I T
S E N D   A Y E S   O C E A N S   T O N E
```

## Puzzle 2-13: Vanishing Acts

Page 96

```
B O R N E   M A R T H A   A C T   M A E
A N A I S   A R A R A T   M O E   T E N S
B L I N K O F A N E Y E   A V E   I S I S
A Y N   E M I L     M A T T E   S M O T E
    S Y R I A   F L A S H I N T H E P A N
A T T E S T   L A K E R   H E R O
L O O T   S C O N E   U L N A   S T O P
A P R I L S H O W E R S   L O W S   A M A
I S M   A E O N S   P E A R   A M M A N
      O T T O   S A L E M   S E I N E
T W O S H A K E S O F A L A M B S T A I L
A R I S E   L E F T Y   A R I A
P I L A R   P I C A   H U M A N   S K I
E S P   S L O T   S H O O T I N G S T A R
S T A S   I D E A   A I M E E   L O N E
    I T E M   M A N S E   P H O N E D
N I N E D A Y W O N D E R   G R E B E
A S T R O   O A S T S   F L O P   C A Y
V E I N   O D D   H O U S E O F C A R D S
A R N O   N E E   E M M I E S   A M A Z E
L E G   O L D   R E A C T S   T I B E R
```

## Puzzle 2-14: Animal Families
Page 98

```
C H O L L A   C A R I B   B R A V E R
A E N E I D   S O L A C E   R E L A X E D
S E D G E O F C R A N E S   A V E R A G E
A L I   B I O N I C   P O I S E   M E T
B E N S   E S N E   H O R N S   M I N E
A D E P T   H E R D O F E L E P H A N T S
      O A R   S E A   F A Y   H O N E S T
P A R T N E R   D I C E D   R O A N
E R A   G E E K   N O R   M A N X   B A T
T R I P O F G O A T S   G O N E   A R N O
R I S E S   A R M Y   P A N G   C R O S S
O V E N   C L A P   C A S T O F H A W K S
L E D   T H E N   B A G   H O R A   N A E
      A R I D   R A M O S   N I P P E R S
S P E C I E   W E N   D O S   T E A
N I D E O F P H E A S A N T S   L I L A C
O N U S   L I L L E   G O E S   L O N E
R O C   G R A P E   C A S K E T   C A N
E L A T I O N   C L U T T E R O F C A T S
R E T I N U E   T O R T E S   R I A L T O
      S E N S E D   S P E A R   E N D E A R
```

## Puzzle 2-15: The Y Factor
Page 100

```
A L G O R E   T I B E T A N   S A G E S T
R E A M E R   A S A R A R E   E N A M O R
C A L E Y A R B O R O U G H   W A P I T I
O R A L   A U N T S   I D A   S L O P
      E V E R S   A I M S   A G O
T A R T A R E   B O R I S Y E L T S I N
E T A   C A B O T   N I N E   D R A N O
E R I N   T I T H E   S C A N T   E G G S
T I N A Y O T H E R S   E L I H U Y A L E
H A S T A   E M I T S   P R I S S E S
      H I E   S C O O T   S O N
A B A L O N E   A M B E R   T H A T S
B U D Y O R K I N   P E T E R Y A R R O W
D E A N   I S L A M   R O D E O   E D N A
E N I D S   A B O O   N O D U S   O T T
L O R E T T A Y O U N G   L L A D R O S
      Y A P   B E A R   H I L D A
T R I S   M E A   S A T A N   R A M A
S E N E C A   T R I S H A Y E A R W O O D
A N I M A L   O B V I A T E   P O I N T E
R E T I R E   M I A S M A S   T E N E T S
```

## Puzzle 2-16: Around the Monopoly Board

Page 102

```
B L A B ■ M O R E ■ D O R M ■ S C A M
E I R E ■ A M E S ■ I D E A ■ H O M E
E V I L ■ N E A T ■ L O N G ■ E M M A
R E A D I N G R A I L R O A D ■ M O D
■ A R E A ■ T O Y ■ Z U L U
C L A M O R ■ P E N ■ E V I D E N C E
O A T E N ■ S O S ■ S E E N ■ G I L A
O I L ■ T I P ■ S T R E E T ■ T U T
T R A P P E R ■ C H A I R ■ H A Y E S
■ N O O N ■ C H O R E ■ B O S C ■
W A T E R ■ S L A V E ■ M A R S H A L
A L I ■ E S C A P E ■ W A G ■ E G O
R I C E ■ H A N S ■ M I X ■ G A S E S
S T A R L I N G ■ F A N ■ S U I T E S
■ V A I L ■ A I R ■ S O A R ■
D O E ■ E L E C T R I C C O M P A N Y
A N N A ■ I D O L ■ N E O N ■ O H I O
S C U D ■ N I N E ■ E T R E ■ R O C K
H E E D ■ G E N E ■ S E E R ■ T Y K E
```

## Puzzle 2-17: Two For Tee

Page 104

```
R A P ■ T H A N ■ B E D ■ B A T M A N
I D O ■ H A R E ■ I M A ■ A P I E C E
T E E T E R T O T T E R ■ L O N E R S
A N T A R E S ■ H U R T ■ C R A T E S
■ M O M ■ A R M Y ■ M O T T ■
E D G E S ■ S L O E ■ S O N ■ U T A H
T I N S E L T O W N ■ W A Y ■ R O V E
C O A T ■ O R E ■ H A T ■ A N G E R
H S T ■ T R U ■ T E A M ■ S H E A R S
■ T O N G U E T W I S T E R ■
C A R R I E ■ B E A N ■ A R M ■ B E D
A X I A L ■ L O N ■ A L A ■ H O N E
S E M I ■ L E A ■ T O P S Y T U R V Y
E D E N ■ I N T ■ R H E A ■ A M A S S
■ T A N S ■ G A B S ■ Q U E ■
S H A R D S ■ O L I O ■ S U N R I S E
P O M A D E ■ T O N Y T H E T I G E R
O R A C L E ■ I R E ■ V O L E ■ G E O
T A N K E D ■ S Y R ■ S O L D ■ Y R S
```

## Puzzle 2-18: Undercover Work
Page 106

## Puzzle 2-19: At the Beanery
Page 108

| B | A | B | A | S | | H | A | G | A | R | | C | A | S | S | | D | I | S | C |
| A | M | U | S | E | | A | D | O | R | E | | A | L | A | I | | E | L | L | A |
| J | U | M | P | I | N | G | J | A | C | K | | W | A | X | M | U | S | E | U | M |
| A | R | S | E | N | E | | S | T | I | N | K | | R | E | I | N | S | U | R | E |
| | | | N | E | E | D | | | N | I | E | L | S | | A | T | E | M | P | O |
| F | I | B | | S | T | R | I | N | G | T | I | E | | | N | O | R | | | |
| O | N | U | S | | S | A | G | A | | S | T | R | A | P | | T | R | A | M | |
| O | R | T | H | O | | M | E | T | A | | H | O | N | E | S | T | | E | G | O |
| T | O | T | E | R | | S | T | U | R | M | | I | N | N | U | E | N | D | O | S |
| E | M | E | R | Y | | | R | E | A | M | | A | N | D | R | E | S | | | |
| D | E | R | M | | G | R | E | E | N | G | A | B | L | E | S | | A | K | I | M |
| | C | A | R | R | O | L | | T | I | L | L | | | S | T | E | N | O | | |
| S | C | U | N | G | I | L | L | I | | C | L | E | F | S | | H | E | L | L | O |
| O | O | P | | B | A | L | I | N | G | | S | E | R | T | | A | S | T | I | R |
| P | O | S | T | | S | E | E | R | S | | P | E | E | P | | T | O | N | E | |
| | | U | P | S | | P | O | L | E | S | T | A | R | S | | N | E | D | | |
| M | A | R | M | O | T | | I | T | S | O | N | | M | O | A | B | | | | |
| A | R | O | U | S | A | L | S | | S | T | R | I | A | | S | C | O | R | E | D |
| J | E | L | L | Y | F | I | S | H | | C | O | F | F | E | E | H | O | U | S | E |
| A | N | E | T | | F | E | E | S | | A | B | A | T | E | | E | L | I | S | E |
| S | A | S | S | | S | U | I | T | | R | E | T | A | R | | T | E | N | O | R |

## Puzzle 2-20: Location, Location, Location!

Page 110

| M | A | D | R | I | D | ■ | ■ | M | A | T | U | R | E | ■ | C | O | P | S | E | S |
|---|---|---|---|---|---|---|---|---|---|---|---|---|---|---|---|---|---|---|---|---|
| O | T | I | O | S | E | ■ | S | E | V | E | N | A | M | ■ | O | R | I | E | N | T |
| C | E | N | T | R | A | L | A | M | E | R | I | C | A | ■ | C | A | N | A | D | A |
| ■ | L | E | A | ■ | N | A | T | O | ■ | ■ | S | I | N | G | A | ■ | A | S | I | T |
| A | I | T | ■ | P | S | I | ■ | ■ | A | T | O | N | A | L | ■ | C | L | O | V | E |
| G | E | T | N | O | ■ | C | L | O | S | I | N | G | T | I | M | E | ■ | N | E | D |
| A | R | E | O | L | A | ■ | E | R | A | T | ■ | ■ | E | M | I | L | I | O | ■ | ■ |
| ■ | ■ | H | A | R | D | E | N | ■ | T | R | A | ■ | ■ | S | L | O | P | E | S | ■ |
| C | A | M | ■ | R | E | A | R | A | X | L | E | S | ■ | A | C | A | D | E | M | E |
| O | M | I | T | ■ | A | L | I | ■ | A | E | S | O | P | S | ■ | R | A | N | E | E |
| M | A | D | R | E | ■ | L | E | O | V | ■ | T | R | O | D | ■ | S | T | E | T | S |
| E | N | D | I | S | ■ | A | R | R | I | V | E | ■ | T | E | E | ■ | E | R | I | N |
| A | T | L | A | S | E | S | ■ | H | E | A | D | S | T | A | R | T | ■ | S | N | O |
| S | E | E | G | E | R | ■ | E | R | N | ■ | A | I | R | M | A | N | ■ | ■ | ■ | ■ |
| ■ | ■ | C | E | N | S | U | S | ■ | ■ | E | A | R | N | ■ | A | M | I | C | E | S |
| T | A | L | ■ | C | E | N | T | E | R | S | T | A | G | E | ■ | E | L | U | D | E |
| O | V | A | T | E | ■ | D | E | V | I | S | E | ■ | ■ | R | E | D | ■ | R | O | W |
| S | I | S | H | ■ | C | O | R | E | D | ■ | ■ | O | N | I | N | ■ | A | R | M | ■ |
| C | A | S | A | B | A | ■ | E | N | D | O | F | T | H | E | A | F | F | A | I | R |
| A | T | E | N | O | R | ■ | O | L | E | O | O | I | L | ■ | T | U | R | N | T | O |
| ■ | E | S | T | O | P | ■ | S | Y | N | O | D | S | ■ | ■ | E | M | O | T | E | D |

### Puzzle 3-1

Page 114

It is not good manners to add cream and sugar to your coffee after you have poured it into your saucer.

### Puzzle 3-2

Page 114

Did you hear about the duck who went to the drugstore to buy some chapstick and asked the pharmacist to put it on his bill?

### Puzzle 3-3

Page 115

The worst thing about new books is that they keep us from reading the old ones. (Joseph Joubert)

### Puzzle 3-4

Page 115

By all means marry. If you get a good mate you will be happy; and if you get a bad one you will become a philosopher.

### Puzzle 3-5

Page 116

Manners will never be fully observed until someone invents self-winding spaghetti and invisible toothpicks.

### Puzzle 3-6

Page 116

If at first you don't succeed, try again. Then quit: No use being a darn fool about it. (W.C. Fields)

## Puzzle 3-7: 21 x 15 Squares

Page 117

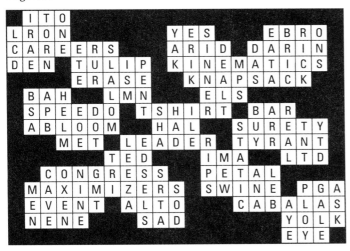

## Puzzle 3-8: 23 x 15 Squares

Page 118

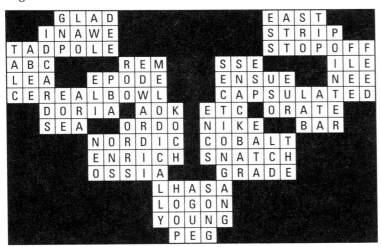

### *Puzzle 3-9: 17 x 19 Squares*

Page 119

### *Puzzle 3-11: 19 x 19 Squares*

Page 121

### *Puzzle 3-10: 23 x 15 Squares*

Page 120

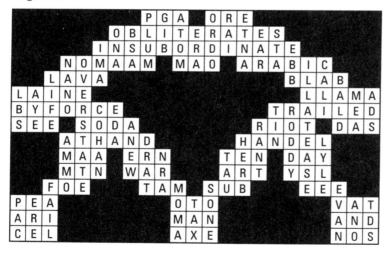

## Puzzle 3-12: Embracing Shadows

Page 122

```
L O V E ■ I S ■ L I K E ■ A ■ W I N D ■ S T I R R I N G
■ T H E ■ G R A S S ■ B E N E A T H ■ T R E E S ■ O N ■
A ■ B L A C K ■ N I G H T ■ Y O U ■ M U S T ■ N O T ■ T
R Y ■ T O ■ M A K E ■ L O V E ■ D E F I N I T E ■ I T
■ I S ■ T H E ■ D I V I N E ■ A C C I D E N T ■ O F ■ L
I F E ■ I F ■ Y O U ■ T R Y ■ T O ■ B E ■ S U R E ■ A
B O U T ■ I T ■ T H E ■ L O N G ■ H O T ■ D A Y ■ O F
D I S A P P O I N T M E N T ■ C O M E S ■ S W I F T L Y
```

A **A**LL IN THE FAMILY  
B **N**OOKS AND CRANNIES  
C **D**ISFIGURING  
D **E**FFECTIVE  
E **R**UFFLED  
F **S**HUTTLE  
G **O**UTLAST  
H **N**ACHO  
I **W**AIT  
J **I**TTY-BITTY  
K **N**ATION  

L **E**VASION  
M **S**HOOT  
N **B**IOS  
O **U**TTER  
P **R**IVETING  
Q **G**OBBLED  
R **O**PTIMISTIC  
S **H**OME SWEET HOME  
T **I**NTERESTED PARTY  
U **O**KEY-DOKEY  
ANDERSON: WINESBURG, OHIO  

## Puzzle 3-13: Tip of the Iceberg

Page 123

```
H O W ■ T R U E ■ I T ■ I S ■ T
H A T ■ W O R D S ■ A R E ■ B U
T ■ T H E ■ V A G U E ■ S H A D
O W S ■ O F ■ T H E ■ V O L U M
E S ■ W E ■ M E A N ■ L I T T L
E ■ A U D I B L E ■ L I N K S ■
T H E Y ■ A R E ■ C H A I N I N
G ■ T O G E T H E R ■ G R E A T
■ I N A U D I B L E ■ F E E L I
N G S ■ A N D ■ P U R P O S E S
```

A **D**OWN AND OUT  
B **R**UGBY  
C **E**GG WHITES  
D **I**MPOLITE  
E **S**ELL OUT  
F **E**LMER FUDD  
G **R**EVIEWING  
H **S**TUBBLE  
I **I**'VE HAD IT  
J **S**OAP  

K **T**HAWS  
L **E**ATS IN  
M **R**ITE  
N **C**HEETAH  
O **A**NKLES  
P **R**USH HOUR  
Q **R**EAL ESTATE  
R **I**N A FOG  
S **E**THAN  
DREISER: SISTER CARRIE

## Puzzle 3-14: A Wicked World
Page 124

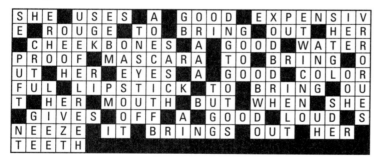

```
  I T   I S   W O N D E R F U L   H O W
M U C H   T I M E   G O O D   P E O P L
E   S P E N D   F I G H T I N G   T H E
D E V I L   I F   T H E Y   W O U L D   O
N L Y   E X P E N D   T H E   S A M E   A
M O U N T   O F   E N E R G Y   L O V I N
G   T H E I R   F E L L O W   M E N   T H
E   D E V I L   W O U L D   D I E   I N
H I S   T R A C K S   O F   E N N U I
```

A **H**OOVED
B **K**OWTOW
C **E**NGLISH CHANNEL
D **L**EFTIST
E **L**UMP OF SUGAR
F **E**NDIVE
G **R**EVIEW
H **S**INNING
I **T**WEEDY
J **O**N THE GOOD SHIP
K **R**ENAME

L **Y**ETI
M **O**FTEN
N **F**OUNDED
O **M**IDDLEWEIGHT
P **Y**OUTHFUL
Q **L**OLLIPOP
R **I**MMIX
S **F**REE LUNCH
T **E**DITH
H. KELLER: STORY OF MY LIFE

## Puzzle 3-15: Looks Are Deceiving
Page 125

```
S H E   U S E S   A   G O O D   E X P E N S I V
E   R O U G E   T O   B R I N G   O U T   H E R
  C H E E K B O N E S   A   G O O D   W A T E R
P R O O F   M A S C A R A   T O   B R I N G   O
U T   H E R   E Y E S   A   G O O D   C O L O R
F U L   L I P S T I C K   T O   B R I N G   O U
T   H E R   M O U T H   B U T   W H E N   S H E
  G I V E S   O F F   A   G O O D   L O U D   S
N E E Z E   I T   B R I N G S   O U T   H E R
T E E T H
```

A **L**IGHTWEIGHT
B **S**HOOFLY
C **A**RPEGGIO
D **F**UMES
E **I**VOR
F **A**UGURED
G **N**EXT TIME
H **G**REENHOUSE
I **I**TCHES
J **A**UVERGNE
K **N**O DOUBT
L **T**OGGLE SWITCH
M **B**UCKAROO

N **O**ZONOSPHERE
O **O**RCHESTRA
P **K**ORDA
Q **O**BEAH
R **F**OISTED
S **I**SSUE
T **N**EPENTHE
U **S**OBER
V **U**RFA
W **L**ODGE
X **T**OO-TOO
Y **S**TUBBORN
L. SAFIAN: GIANT BOOK OF INSULTS

## Puzzle 3-16: What's In a Name?

Page 126

```
O R I G I N A L L Y   C A L L E D   E R N E S T   P
O N T I F E X   A F T E R   T H E   A W K W A R D   Y
O U N G   H E R O   O F   T H I S   P O S T H U M O U
S L Y   P U B L I S H E D   N O V E L   I T   I S   T
H E   S A G A   O F   F O U R   G E N E R A T I O N S
  O F   A   F A M I L Y   G I V E N   T O   M U C H
B A D   L U C K   G O O D   F O R T U N E   S M I L E
S   I N   T H E   E N D   A N D   T H E   A U T H O R
  F O U N D   A   P A S S A G E   F R O M   T H E   B
I B L E   T O   S Y M B O L I Z E   H I S   T A L E
```

**A** SHAPE UP
**B** AXIOM
**C** MUFFIN TIN
**D** ULTERIOR
**E** EFFIGY
**F** LOAD OF THIS
**G** BENCH
**H** UNUSUAL
**I** TITLE PAGE
**J** LOOSEY GOOSEY
**K** ETON
**L** RHESUS
**M** THIMBLE THEATRE
**N** HEDGE ONES
**O** EFFORT
**P** WHISKBROOM

**Q** ASKEW
**R** YOUNG
**S** OVERACTED
**T** FONZ
**U** ARMOR
**V** LAND AND SEA
**W** LIGHTS OUT
**X** FAITHFUL
**Y** LITTLE LAMB
**Z** EDIT
**AA** SAVINGS AND LOAN
**BB** HYDROPHOBIC
SAMUEL BUTLER: THE WAY OF ALL FLESH

# Appendix B
# Working Non-Crossword Puzzles

• • • • • • • • • • • • • • • • • • • • • • • • • • • • • • • • • • • • • • • • • • • • • • • •

### In This Chapter

▶ Discovering cryptograms

▶ Giving some structure to diagramless puzzles

▶ Getting the lowdown on acrostics

• • • • • • • • • • • • • • • • • • • • • • • • • • • • • • • • • • • • • • • • • • • • • • • •

*I*n this appendix, I show you how to work the puzzles you find in Part III, namely the cryptogram, diagramless, and acrostic.

## *Cracking the Cryptogram Code*

Cryptograms are all about letter replacement. Letters in cryptograms have been switched around, creating a funky-looking message that you need to decipher.

In a cryptogram, every letter stands for a different one (and only one) throughout the message. For example, "B" may represent "T" throughout the cryptogram, and "T" may mean "C." Although the pattern of the sentence looks familiar, the "words" read as if they are in some kind of secret code. Under each of the letters in the code, you see a space. As you decipher each letter in the code, you write it in the space. After you fill in each of the spaces, you have decoded the cryptogram, and you see a message in the spaces under the cryptogram letters.

The "code" changes from puzzle to puzzle, as though the alphabet flies up in the air, with the letters landing in different places, for each puzzle. Unfortunately, cracking the code on one puzzle doesn't give you a Rosetta Stone that you can apply to all other cryptograms.

Cryptogram words are exact replicas of the actual words they disguise. For example, if you see a three-letter word as part of a cryptogram, you know that a three-letter word appears in the quote or phrase hidden within the puzzle.

Typically, a cryptogram message is a quotation (complete with punctuation). The author's name may appear at the end of the cryptogram.

Note that some cryptograms offer a hint by revealing the identity of one of the disguised letters. You may want to ignore the help, or you may welcome a helping hand until you get the hang of it.

To work the cryptogram, follow these steps:

1. **Jot down the alphabet on scrap paper.**

   You need to do a little prep work first. You use this list to keep tabs on the letters you have already matched up and, consequently, which letters are still "unused."

**2. Scan the cryptogram for one-letter words, which are typically A or I.**

Of course, you won't know which of the letters is the right one until you work a little more into the puzzle, but if you have a good feeling about one letter over the other, go ahead and pencil it in.

**3. After you crack the code on a letter, pencil in all occurrences of that letter in the puzzle. For example, where you find L to replace A, identify all the As as Ls through the cryptogram.**

And I do mean pencil! You may need to experiment many times before you actually match up a letter. Don't attempt to work a cryptogram with a pen unless you really enjoy the smell of corrector fluid.

**4. Scan the cryptogram for two-letter words, then three-letter words, and so on, matching letters up as you go.**

With each grouping of words, the message should come more and more into focus.

Table B-1 lists the most common words that appear in cryptograms; the words in each length category are listed in frequency of appearance.

| Table B-1 | Cryptogram Repeaters |
|---|---|
| **Number of Letters** | **Repeaters** |
| 1 | A and I |
| 2 | IT, IN, IS, IF, AT, ON, TO, OF, AS, and AN |
| 3 | THE, AND, FOR, ARE, and BUT |
| 4 | THAT, THIS, THAN, and THEN |

You also need to be on the lookout for the following patterns as you work your way through the cryptogram:

✔ **Apostrophes:** Where an apostrophe appears near the end of a word followed by a single letter, your choice on that last letter is limited to S or T (or sometimes D). When it follows a single letter, that letter must be I to give you I'D, I'LL, or I'VE. Where an apostrophe is followed by two letters, your choice opens to 'LL, 'RE, and 'VE.

✔ **Double letters:** Check for EE, OO, FF, LL, SS, TT, and MM, in that order.

✔ **Final letters:** Check for E, T, S, D, N, and R, in this order, at the end of words.

✔ **Initial letters:** Check for T, A, O, M, H, and W at the beginning of words.

✔ **Suffixes:** Check for ING and LY at the end of longer words.

The cryptogram's alphabet may not contain all 26 letters of the standard alphabet, depending on which letters show up in the message. A cryptographer may try to confuse you by deliberately eliminating some letters from the message altogether.

The key to cryptogram decoding, according to Laura Z. Hobson, author of the classic novel *Gentleman's Agreement* as well as scores of cryptograms, is to bear in mind that the most commonly used letter in English is E. Experienced crypt solvers often begin the decoding process by looking for E first. The most popular consonant is T. After you determine which letters represent E and T, you can move on to the next group of commonly used letters. Expert consensus ranks O and S in that category. M follows, according to Hobson. Other runners-up are A, I, and N.

# Attempting the Diagramless

In a diagramless puzzle, you get Across and Down clues, but no grid to fill with the answers to the clues. Your job is to sketch out a grid (according to the dimensions shown at the top of the puzzle) by using the answers to the clues.

One of the neat aspects of conventional crosswords is that you don't need any special equipment to play the game. As long as you have a writing utensil, you can play.

When you tackle the diagramless puzzle, however, you need some additional equipment. Although some people solve the diagramless in their heads, most acrossionados like to see the grid on paper. Of course, you can use the back of an envelope in a pinch (I have). But in order to be sure that you're on the right square, you may need a supply of graph paper and a clean eraser.

Try to keep two sheets of graph paper handy while solving a diagramless puzzle. With the extra sheet, you have the opportunity to experiment as you try to uncover a general pattern.

Some sources supply a blank grid for you on the page in the correct dimensions, so that all you have to do is carefully plot the pattern. But if you don't have a black-and-white grid pattern to look at, the first step in attempting the diagramless is to refer to the dimensions indicated at the top of the puzzle. The dimensions look like a math formula, as in "15 × 15." For a 15 × 15 puzzle, draw a frame that measures 15 squares across and down on your graph paper to help you focus on the emerging pattern. If the dimensions are something like 15 × 17, then the first number is the Across dimension, and the second number is the Down dimension.

After you have either located or prepared your grid, you need to look for another piece of critical information. The puzzle will tell you where the first Across entry begins. (Without this piece of info, the puzzle would be impossible to solve.) Go ahead and write the number 1 in the appropriate square.

Your next step is to determine the length of the first Across entry. Unlike a crossword, you want to approach the diagramless from 1 Across for best results. Without a grid, you don't have that visual reference to how many letters are in each word and where the entries belong. Instead, you have two ways to determine how many letters appear in the 1 Across entry:

- ✔ Look at the number of the second Across clue. If it's 6, for example, then you can surmise that the entry for 1 Across contains five letters.
- ✔ Check that Down clues 1 through 5 don't appear in the Across column.

If the second Across clue is 6 Across, you know that the first word consists of five letters. The five Down clues, from 1 through 5, that don't have an Across function confirm your assumption.

Fill in a black square to the left of and above each number that appears in both Across and Down columns.

What distinguishes 1 Across from every other Across clue is that the solver can be certain that each letter of its entry serves as the first letter of a Down entry. In this case, you can blacken the sixth square after filling in the Across entry. Insert the numbers 1 through 5 in the appropriate squares and try to solve as many of the first five Down clues as you can. Before long, you create a block of answers that sets the puzzle on its path.

Don't worry about the clues: Diagramless clues are simpler than those of the average crossword because the constructor doesn't want to compound the handicap.

Because diagramless puzzles don't usually follow the square shape of a crossword, you can't make assumptions about where answers fall in the grid until you have made some progress. But you do have some information on your side:

✔ **You know that the grid is usually symmetrical.** In most cases, the pattern on top is a mirror image of the bottom. After you have plotted the pattern for the top half, you can transfer it to the bottom, and the other way around, too. Less often, the symmetry is left to right.

✔ **You know that the second Across answer follows 1 Across somehow.** In the standard crossword (and in most diagramless puzzles), the second Across entry appears directly to the right of the first entry in the grid in the same line. But the diagramless makes an exception: The second Across entry may appear one line down and to the left of 1 Across. As entries emerge, you can determine where the second Across entry belongs in the grid.

What if the second Across clue doesn't appear in the Down column? If the 6 Across entry isn't included in the Down column, for example, your solving takes a different direction, because now you know that the second Across answer appears directly *below* 1 Across. Chances are that the answer to 6 Across may begin to emerge after you fill in some of the first five Down entries. If the second Across number also appears in the Down column along with two more Down clues, then it most likely appears to the right of 1 Across, following the typical crossword format. Following the example, 6 appears in both Across and Down, while 7 and 8 are only clued Down. The third Across clue, then, is 9.

Even before you proceed with the second Across answer, I recommend jotting down any answers that pop out at you next to the lists of clues. Scanning all the way through the Across and Down clues and writing down as many entries as you can beside the clues is helpful. Islands of answers may emerge this way. Sometimes you can solve separate parts of the puzzle and unite them later. Only confirmed acrossionados try to discern the pattern before working the clues. The fun of the diagramless lies in coordinating the two as you solve.

Every entry that appears in both the Across and Down columns in a diagramless has a black square to its left and above it. Every entry that appears only in the Down clues has a black square above it and below its final letter.

After you see a black-and-white pattern start to emerge at the top part of your graph, you can safely turn your grid upside down and sketch in the mirror image below. In fact, if you find the entries easier to solve at the bottom, you may want to approach the diagramless from the bottom.

# Solving an Acrostic

A truly great puzzle is not only fun, but also enlightening. Rather than a random collection of words, the acrostic grid contains an excerpt from a written work. Entries in the grid only read across, not down, moving from top row to bottom, reading left to right.

The acrostic grid is accompanied by a word list. After you solve the words in the word list, the initial letters of the answer words spell out the author and title of the work that is quoted in the grid.

Technically, the double aspect of the acrostic describes the way the two basic elements of the puzzle interact. You work with the same two variables of the crossword — the grid and clues — but in a new way. You use a two-part solving process for an acrostic:

1. **First, you have to solve the clues in the word list.**

   The clues are not hard at all. In fact, in the case of a missing word, the acrostic constructor may cite the source. Instead of numbers, you find the word list (about two dozen words) sorted by letters from A through Z.

2. **Next, you transfer the letters you have so far from the word list into their assigned squares in the grid.**

   Every letter serves in the grid as well as in an answer on the word list. As you fill in the word list, you note a number beneath each letter that indicates its placement in the grid. After you fill in the squares, a quotation of about 25 words emerges as you read the grid from left to right.

Black squares in the acrostic grid serve as spaces between words. Every white square contains a number and letter, which corresponds to a letter in one of the words in the word list.

The acrostic clues don't contain any tricks: They are completely straightforward. If you look up the answers in the dictionary, you find yourself staring right at the clues. For example, when a clue reads "Unsteady" followed by six dashes, the answer is a commonly used synonym like WOBBLY. When the answer in a word list consists of more than one word, the constructor indicates that fact in parentheses, as in "Insectivore, also called potamogale (5, 5)" for OTTER SHREW.

Acrostic clues may require some interpretation. When you have a clue such as "Thumb" followed by nine dashes, do you stare at your fingers, or do you take it for a verb, as in HITCHHIKE? Words from acrostic clues are in the dictionary, but you may have to move beyond the first definition you find.

Words in the quotation may run on into two rows. The beginning of a word may appear on one line at the far right, and the final letters appear in the next line below to the far left. That split includes words of one syllable, as in TH on the top line and ERE on the next line, below and to the left, to read as THERE. Only a black square indicates the end of the word, not the outside frame of the grid, as per the standard crossword.

The empty grid can give you some helpful hints about the way the quotation unfolds:

✔ **Single-letter words:** When you see a white square between two black squares, the two obvious choices in the English language are A and I. (On the rare occasion, you may come across an initial, as in "J. D." Salinger.) If multiple single-letter words appear in the grid, odds are that the excerpt is in the first person, and you can safely insert I in various parts of each place.

✔ **Three-letter words:** Most often, you're looking at THE or AND.

# Notes

# Notes

# Notes

# Notes

# Notes

# Playing games is really fun... The Dummies Way™!

Pressman®
©1998 Pressman Toy Corporation, New York, NY 10010

### Crosswords For Dummies™ Game

You don't have to know how to spell to have a great time. Place a word strip on the board so that it overlaps another word or creates a new one. Special squares add to the fun. The first player to use up all their word strips wins!
For 2 to 4 players.

### Trivia For Dummies™ Game

You're guaranteed to have an answer every time! Each player gets 10 cards that contain the answer to every question. Act quickly and be the first player to throw down the correct answer and move closer to the finish line!
For 3 or 4 players.

### Charades For Dummies™ Game

Act out one-word charades: when other players guess them, they move ahead. The special cards keep the game full of surprises. The first player around the board wins.
For 3 or 4 players.

----For Dummies and The Dummies Way are trademarks or registered trademarks of IDG Books Worldwide, Inc.

YOUR ONLINE RESOURCE

# WWW.DUMMIES.COM

# Discover Dummies™ Online!

The *Dummies* Web Site is your fun and friendly online resource for the latest information about *...For Dummies*® books on all your favorite topics. From cars to computers, wine to Windows, and investing to the Internet, we've got a shelf full of *...For Dummies* books waiting for you!

## Ten Fun and Useful Things You Can Do at www.dummies.com

1. Register this book and win!
2. Find and buy the *...For Dummies* books you want online.
3. Get ten great *Dummies Tips™* every week.
4. Chat with your favorite *...For Dummies* authors.
5. Subscribe free to *The Dummies Dispatch™* newsletter.
6. Enter our sweepstakes and win cool stuff.
7. Send a free cartoon postcard to a friend.
8. Download free software.
9. Sample a book before you buy.
10. Talk to us. Make comments, ask questions, and get answers!

Jump online to these ten fun and useful things at
**http://www.dummies.com/10useful**

SURF THE NET

WWW.DUMMIES.COM

For other technology titles from IDG Books Worldwide, go to
**www.idgbooks.com**

Not online yet? It's easy to get started with *The Internet For Dummies*®, 5th Edition, or *Dummies 101*®: *The Internet For Windows*® *98*, available at local retailers everywhere.

**IDG BOOKS** WORLDWIDE®

Find other *...For Dummies* books on these topics:
Business • Careers • Databases • Food & Beverages • Games • Gardening • Graphics • Hardware
Health & Fitness • Internet and the World Wide Web • Networking • Office Suites
Operating Systems • Personal Finance • Pets • Programming • Recreation • Sports
Spreadsheets • Teacher Resources • Test Prep • Word Processing

# IDG BOOKS WORLDWIDE. BOOK REGISTRATION

**Register This Book and Win!**

## We want to hear from you!

Visit **http://my2cents.dummies.com** to register this book and tell us how you liked it!

- Get entered in our monthly prize giveaway.

- Give us feedback about this book — tell us what you like best, what you like least, or maybe what you'd like to ask the author and us to change!

- Let us know any other *...For Dummies*® topics that interest you.

Your feedback helps us determine what books to publish, tells us what coverage to add as we revise our books, and lets us know whether we're meeting your needs as a *...For Dummies* reader. You're our most valuable resource, and what you have to say is important to us!

Not on the Web yet? It's easy to get started with *Dummies 101*®*: The Internet For Windows*® *98* or *The Internet For Dummies*®, 5th Edition, at local retailers everywhere.

Or let us know what you think by sending us a letter at the following address:

*...For Dummies* Book Registration
Dummies Press
7260 Shadeland Station, Suite 100
Indianapolis, IN  46256-3917
Fax 317-596-5498

**...FOR DUMMIES**™

**BESTSELLING BOOK SERIES**